PHOTO GUIDE TO
FISHES *of* *the* MALDIVES
RUDIE H. KUITER

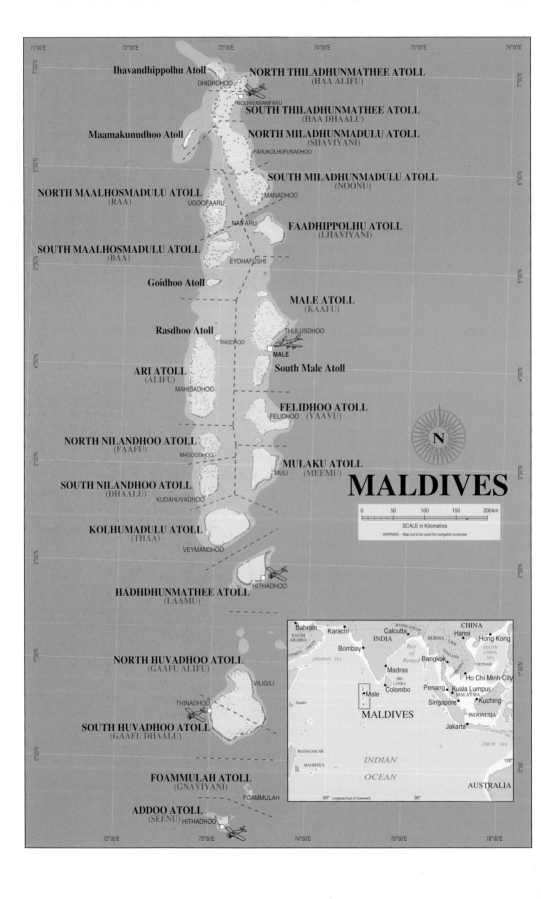

PHOTO GUIDE TO
FISHES *of the* MALDIVES

RUDIE H. KUITER

ATOLL
EDITIONS

First published in 1998 by
ATOLL EDITIONS
PO Box 113, Apollo Bay
VIC 3233, Australia
Fax Int +61 3 5237 6332
www.atolleditions.com.au

Reprinted in 2001, 2002

Publisher: *Tim Godfrey*
Design, indexer and typesetting: *Rudie H. Kuiter.*
Reproduction: *Color Point Security, Melbourne.*
Printed and Bound in: *Singapore*

National Library of Australia
Cataloguing-in-Publication data

Kuiter, R.H.
Photo guide to Fishes of the Maldives

Includes index
ISBN 1 876410 18 3

1. Fishes-Maldives-Identification.
2. Fishes-Classification-Pictorial works.
i. Title

TABLE OF CONTENTS

ABOUT THE MALDIVES 6
    Geography 6
    Geology 6
    Water temperatures 7
    Weather 7
    Currents 8
    Protected Marine Areas 8
INTRODUCTION 9
ABOUT THE BOOK 9
    Species order 10
EVOLUTION - SPECIES CREATION 11
    General 11
    Adaptation 11
    Faunas Dividing 12
    Scientific & Common Names 13
ABOUT FISHES 14
    Colour and Camouflage 14
    Colour patterns 15
    Mimicry 16
    Cleaning Stations 17
    Symbiotic Relationships 17
    Spawning & Parental Care 18
    Development & Age 19
    Measurements 20
    External features 21
    Shapes of fishes 24

FAMILIES & SPECIES ACCOUNTS 24

MORAY EELS - MURAENIDAE		24
SNAKE & WORM EELS - OPHICHTHIDAE		29
GARDEN EELS - CONGRIDAE		31
HERRINGS - CLUPEIDAE		32
HARDYHEADS - ATHERINIDAE		32
HALFBEAKS - HEMIRAMPHIDAE		33
NEEDLEFISHES - BELONIDAE		34
EELTAIL CATFISHES - PLOTOSIDAE		35
LINGS - OPHIDIIDAE		35
ANGLERFISHES - ANTENNARIIDAE		36

LIZARDFISHES - SYNODONTIDAE		38
FLASHLIGHT FISHES - ANOMALOPIDAE		40
SQUIRRELFISHES - HOLOCENTRIDAE-1		41
SOLDIERFISHES - HOLOCENTRIDAE-2		45
SEAMOTHS - PEGASIDAE		48
TRUMPETFISHES - AULOSTOMIDAE		48
FLUTEMOUTHS - FISTULARIIDAE		49
GHOSTPIPEFISHES - SOLENOSTOMIDAE		49
PIPEFISHES - SYNGNATHIDAE		50
FLYING GURNARDS - DACTYLOPTERIDAE		54
LIONFISHES - SCORPAENIDAE-1		55
SCORPIONFISHES - SCORPAENIDAE-2		57
WASPFISHES - TETRAROGIDAE		59
FLATHEADS - PLATYCEPHALIDAE		60
SOAPFISHES - SERRANIDAE-1		61
GROUPERS - SERRANIDAE-2		63
BASSLETS - SERRANIDAE-3		73
DOTTYBACKS - PSEUDOCHROMIDAE		77
LONGFINS - PLESIOPIDAE		77
TRIPLE TAILS - LOBOTIDAE		78
TRUMPETERS & GRUNTERS - TERAPONTIDAE		78

FLAGTAILS - KUHLIIDAE		79
BIGEYES - PRIACANTHIDAE		79
CARDINALFISHES - APOGONIDAE		80
TILEFISHES - MALACANTHIDAE		89
REMORAS - ECHENEIDAE		91
JACKS & TREVALLIES - CARANGIDAE		92
SILVER BATFISHES - MONODACTYLIDAE		97
PURSEMOUTHS - GERREIDAE		97
SPINECHEEKS - NEMIPTERIDAE		99
EMPERORS - LETHRINIDAE		100
SWEETLIPS - HAEMULIDAE		104
SNAPPERS - LUTJANIDAE		106
FUSILIERS - CAESIONIDAE		112
GOATFISHES - MULLIDAE		115
BULLSEYES - PEMPHERIDIDAE		119
RUDDERFISHES - KYPHOSIDAE		120
BUTTERFLYFISHES - CHAETODONTIDAE		121
ANGELFISHES - POMACANTHIDAE		130
BATFISHES - EPHIPPIDAE		135
HAWKFISHES - CIRRHITIDAE		137
ANEMONEFISHES - POMACENTRIDAE-1		140

HUMBUGS -
POMACENTRIDAE-2 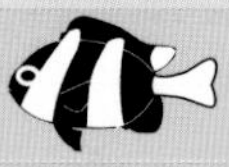
141

PULLERS -
POMACENTRIDAE-3 
142

DAMSELS -
POMACENTRIDAE-4 
145

SERGEANTS -
POMACENTRIDAE-5 
149

FARMER DAMSELS -
POMACENTRIDAE-6 
151

BARRACUDAS -
SPHYRAENIDAE 
153

MULLETS -
MUGILIDAE 
154

SAND WRASSES -
LABRIDAE-1 
155

SAND-REEF WRASSES -
LABRIDAE-2 
160

CLEANER WRASSES -
LABRIDAE-3 
166

LUNATE-TAILED WRASSES -
LABRIDAE-4 
168

SMALL-MOUTHED WRASSES -
LABRIDAE-5 
171

CAVE WRASSES -
LABRIDAE-6 
173

MAORI AND THICKLIP WRASSES -
LABRIDAE-7 
173

HOGFISHES -
LABRIDAE-8 
178

PARROTFISHES -
SCARIDAE 
180

GRUBFISHES -
PINGUIPEDIDAE 
188

SAND DIVERS -
TRICHONOTIDAE 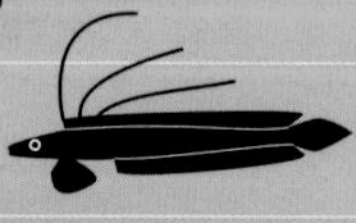
189

TRIPLEFINS -
TRIPTERYGIIDAE 
190

SABRETOOTH BLENNIES -
BLENNIIDAE-1 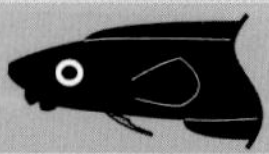
191

REEF BLENNIES -
BLENNIIDAE-2 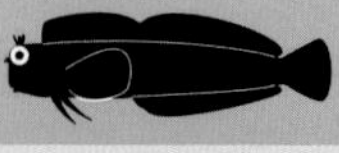
193

DRAGONETS - CALLIONYMIDAE 197

SHRIMPGOBIES - GOBIIDAE-1 198

SAND GOBIES - GOBIIDAE-2 202

REEF GOBIES - GOBIIDAE-3 206

SLEEPER GOBIES - GOBIIDAE-4 212

DART GOBIES & WORM GOBIES - MICRODESMIDAE 216

MOORISH IDOLS - ZANCLIDAE 218

SURGEONFISHES - ACANTHURIDAE 218

RABBITFISHES - SIGANIDAE 228

TUNAS & MACKERELS - SCOMBRIDAE 230

LEFT-EYED FLOUNDERS - BOTHIDAE 231

RIGHT-EYED FLOUNDERS - PLEURONECTIDAE 231

SOLES - SOLEIDAE 232

FILEFISHES - MONACANTHIDAE 232

TRIGGERFISHES - BALISTIDAE 235

BOXFISHES - OSTRACIIDAE 242

PUFFERFISHES - TETRAODONTIDAE 243

PORCUPINEFISHES - DIODONTIDAE 248

INDEX TO FAMILIES AND SPECIES 250
FURTHER READING 257
ACKNOWLEDGEMENTS 257

ABOUT THE MALDIVES
by Tim Godfrey

GEOGRAPHY

The Republic of the Maldives lies south-west of the southern tip of India, and spans a vast area of the west Indian Ocean from 7° 6' 30" N to just south of the equator, 0° 42' 30" S, and between longitudes 72° 32' 30" E and 73° 46' 15" E. It forms the central part of an underwater mountain range stretching for over 2000 kilometres from the Laccadives (islands of Lakshadsweep) in the north, to the Chagos Archipelago in the South. The area of the Maldives is about 90,000 square kilometres, yet less than an estimated 0.5 % is dry land. There are 1190 islands with some kind of vegetation on them, whether grass, bushes or trees, 990 of which are uninhabited and 200 inhabited. An estimated 200,000 people make up the local population but many are concentrated in or near Malé, the capital. The islands are divided into 26 geographic atolls but for convenience, these are divided into 19 administrative groups. The atolls vary in size from the tiny atoll of Thoddoo with a diameter of 2.5 kilometres and only one island, to the great Huvadhoo Atoll with a length of 82 kilometres, a width of 67 kilometres and comprising 244 islands. Most of the north and central part of the Maldives is made up of two separate chains of atolls separated by a plateau with depths ranging between 300 metres and 500 metres. In the south, the atolls form a single chain and are separated by wider and deeper channels. The widest channel, Huvadhoo Kandu, otherwise known as the One and Half Degree Channel is 96 kilometre across with depths reaching 900 metres. On both the east and west sides of the archipelago depths of 2000 metres can occur within 5.5 kilometres of the outer reefs. The inside of the atolls are usually at depths between 30 and 50 metres, but depths up to 90 metres occur in Huvadhoo Atoll.

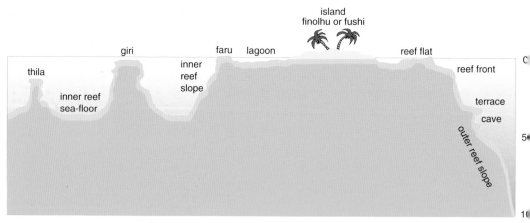

Cross section of a coral reef in the Maldives.

GEOLOGY

Charles Darwin proposed that the atolls of the Maldives developed as the mountain range gradually subsided into the sea or sea levels rose. The fringing reefs surrounding these mountains built up and became more distant from the centre of the range until there was nothing left but a circle of reefs enclosing a lagoon, called an atoll.

Coral reefs are created by a tiny animal, called a polyp, that secretes a hard limestone skeleton and provides the reef's framework. Fragile branching coral may grow between 20 to 30 centimetres per year, while massive boulder-shaped coral may grow only a few millimetres per year. Coralline algae, which thrives in areas exposed to wave action and places too deep and dark for the coral, cement the framework of dead and broken coral together forming a solid limestone base. During ice ages, rise and falls in sea-levels forced migration of reef building corals to colonise new areas. At some stage during these times, reefs were left high out of the water.

The limestone reefs were readily eroded by fresh water and this led to the formation of caves and canyons of all shapes and sizes. After they were again flooded by the sea, marine life re-established itself and layers of coral and coralline algae continued to grow upon the eroded gutters and valleys. These eroded substrata largely govern the shapes of modern reefs. Today, many of these features remain submerged providing divers with spectacular natural attractions.

The outer reef slope of the atolls are generally distinguished by greater depths and increased clarity of water. The visibility may exceed 50 metres. Looking down the reef slope, the coral communities change rapidly with increasing depth. At depths greater than 20 metres, wave surge is non-existent and extensive coral growth may occur to depths of 50 metres and more. Light availability is the main factor limiting the range of the coral here. The upper parts of the outer reef slope may be affected by wave action, restricting the growth of more delicate plate coral. Coral growth can be wiped out in a single freak storm in this zone. In areas less exposed to wave action, extensive stands of staghorn corals can dominate. A great variety of fish life occurs among the coral in this zone.

The reef front is the part of the reef which takes the full force of the ocean swells. The coral here tends to be gnarled and stunted as a result of the pounding by waves.

The reef flats can range in width from a few metres to a few kilometres. Rainwater can damage or completely destroy the coral in this zone if heavy or cyclonic rainfall coincides with very low tides.

Lagoons with good circulation of water may have large stands of branching corals growing on the sand. Lagoons can trap many fish varieties as the tide recedes.

On the inner reef slope, coral growth may be rich if the slope is not too steep. Steep or vertical slopes may be bare. Many interesting caves, overhangs and gullies can occur in this zone. Rising from the floor are separate coral reefs or coral patches, known as giris and thilas. The giris nearly reach the surface, whereas the thilas lay below at depths between five and 15 metres.

There are many words in Dhivehi, the local language, used to describe islands and reefs. A fushi is a big island usually on the outside reef of the atoll and a finolhu is an island with few or no coconut trees. Dhoo and Huraa are other words for an island. Reefs are usually called farus or falhus. A faru, is a reef partially exposed at low tide and a falhu is often a reef encircling a lagoon, sometimes with one or more islands inside. Gaa and haa are other words used to describe coral reefs.

WATER TEMPERATURES

Ocean water temperatures rarely vary beyond 27 – 30° C although a thermocline can sometimes be experienced at depths below 20 metres. During hot periods, water temperatures inside the lagoons increases measurably, influencing water temperatures inside the atolls.

WEATHER

The weather in the Maldives is determined to a large extent by the monsoon circulation. Each year there are two monsoon seasons, the north-east monsoon, Iruvaa, and the south-west monsoon, Hulhagu. The prevailing winds can become quite strong and are from the N-NE-E during the north-east monsoon and the SW-W-NW during the south-west monsoon.

According to the traditional Maldivian calendar, the Iruvaa begins on December 10 with typically strong, unsettled winds and rough seas that gradually travel down the Maldives from the north. It is divided into nine 'Nakaiy', or periods, with the last Nakaiy finishing on April 7. The Iruvaa brings the driest period – the air having a comparatively short sea track compared with that during the remainder of the year.

The Hulhagu begins on April 8 and starts with a storm and rain moving up from the south. It is followed by a brief period of calm winds. It has 18 Nakaiy with the last one finishing on December 9.

The hot season is in March and April, while the wet season is from June to September. Gales and moderate to rough seas are common during the wet season and cloudy days are more frequent.

There is considerable variation in climate between the northern and southern atolls in the Maldives. In the south the rainfall is greater and temperatures are less extreme, as the seasons are less evident close to the equator.

CURRENTS

The exposure of the Maldives to the vast Indian Ocean ensures that an immense body of water is constantly flowing across the plateau on which these atolls are built. Oceanic currents are largely influenced by the direction of the trade winds. They flow from the NE to the SW during the Iruvaa and from the SW to the NE during the Hulhagu. They are of great strength and currents in the channels near Male have been recorded at four knots or more. Tidal currents flow according to the height of the tide and the direction of the prevailing winds and are said to be much weaker than oceanic currents, though they cause velocity variations in the flow. At atoll passages, current streams can be quite irregular due to the islands, reefs and sandy shoals.

PROTECTED MARINE AREAS

Protected Marine Areas were established in the Maldives in response to concern of overfishing for sharks, including at popular diving locations. Since 1995, there are 15 areas set aside, all within the major tourist atolls, and protection was widened to include all forms of marine life from collection or damage. Fishing is not allowed in these designated areas and it is prohibited to anchor, dump rubbish, collect coral, aquarium fish or any other marine organisms. This is the first step in protecting popular dive sites and if successful more areas are expected to be nominated in the future. Grouper fishing and collecting of aquarium specimens, including fishes and invertebrates, has expanded rapidly over the last few years and demand will increase. Removal of reef fishes such as groupers that are often many years old, depletes an area quickly and some species could disappear all together. The effect would become obvious with most of the larger and colourful species gone. The benefits of protecting these area is yet to be fully realised.

LIST OF PROTECTED AREAS

North Malé Atoll: Makunudhoo Kandu, Rasfari, H.P. Reef, Banana Reef, Kuda, Lions, Hans Hass Place.
South Malé Atoll: Embudhoo Kandu, Guraidhoo Kandu.
Ari Atoll: Maaya Thila, Orimas Thila, Fish Head, Kudarah Thila.
Felidhoo Atoll: Devana Kandu.
Faadhippolhu Atoll (Lhaviyani): Fushifaru Thila.
(For detailed maps of these areas, see: Dive Maldives, by Tim Godfrey, published by Atoll Editions, 32 Seymour Cres, Apollo Bay, 3233, Victoria, Australia.)

INTRODUCTION

Divers visiting tropical reefs for the first time, can be overwhelmed by the myriad of colours and movement when watching fish, schools feeding or brightly colourful individuals amongst corals. Maldives reefs are exceptionally rich with fish life, often clouding the water column to the surface along the reef edges. Fish-watching or photographing them underwater has become one of the most popular pastimes with the tourist diver. Nowadays, almost every diver has a camera and for the majority of divers fish are their main subjects. For some, these are the largest such as Whale Sharks, whilst for others, it is the interesting small goby that is targeted. Shooting fish in the Maldives is with a camera only, spearguns are not allowed. Divers are taking more and more notice of the smaller species that live in the reefs, with the added excitement of finding new species. This book encompasses all bony fishes know from the Maldives Archipelago likely to be noticed by divers, including the smallest species. In all, about one-thousand different fishes are known from the area, including sharks and pelagic fishes that occasionally visit reefs. As diving and fish-watching is relatively new, more will undoubtedly turn up as time goes by. Excluded are the cartilaginous (non-bony) ones, such as sharks and rays, that are well covered in other books (see further reading).

Numerous photographic books on diving and marine life in the Maldives have been published by diver-photographers, but they often include underwater pictures taken elsewhere. Such photographs may show fish species that are not known from the Maldives. The most reliable source on Maldives fishes was published by Randall & Anderson in 1993, based on specimens and positive sighting or photographs from the actual area of the Maldives, including notes on doubtfully recorded species. This list formed the basis for this book, but many new records are added since. Much of the Maldives Archipelago remains unexplored by fish experts and new areas visited usually results in several new records. Many of the photographs taken for this book represent new records for the Maldives. In all, about 1,200 photographs were used, illustrating almost 700 species.

Oceanic locations, such as the Maldives, support fewer habitats compared to large continental land masses and usually are less diverse for species. Generally, the more remote, the less diverse, but the Maldives stretches over a large area from north to south, crossing the equator, supporting a rich ecology that balances out the lack of diversity with abundance of particular species. The colourful species are especially noted when schooling in massive numbers, forming a spectacular sight rarely seen elsewhere and is a major attraction to divers from all over the world.

ABOUT THE BOOK

This book serves primarily as a photographic fish-identification guide for divers. Of course, it is of interest to aquarists and everybody else interested in fishes. Many species have geographical variations, meaning that a particular species looks slightly different between different areas, and this particularly applies in the Maldives. Some of such species may even prove to be valid species. For this reason, pictures for this book were taken in the Maldives as much as possible, giving additional value to the book. A photograph taken in a particular locality represents a record, even if the scientific name changes in the future. The entire book is a collection of photographs that show species in living colours, which is very useful for taxonomists who often work with preserved material. Photographs taken outside the Maldives are captioned with their locality. Almost every picture was taken in the wild, only a few in aquariums. The book includes the work of many contributing photographers and they are credited with each of their pictures. Several photographers contributed with many photographs, and they are featured on the back cover.

SPECIES ORDER (CLASSIFICATION)

Species are arranged in an order generally accepted by fish taxonomists: starting with the ones considered the most primitive, and ending with those most advanced, in evolutionary terms. However, as this book serves mainly as a photo guide, and images are the main tool to identify particular species, some compromises were made to put more similar species closer together to make comparison easier. This book is not about systematics and family is the highest level, each containing genera, and each genera containing species. Each level or group, family, genus, species, etc, is called a taxon, and scientist working these groups are called taxonomists. A particular species is a life form that reproduces itself and keeps its distinctive identity. Those species that most recently have evolved separately from a common ancestor are known as sibling species. They can be very similar and often there is some debate about them being a valid species in their own right, a subspecies, or merely a geographical variation. It is generally accepted that when two such forms occur together and maintain their identity they are regarded as good species. Sometimes sibling species occur in mixed pairs and may produce infertile hybrids (Fig. 1.).

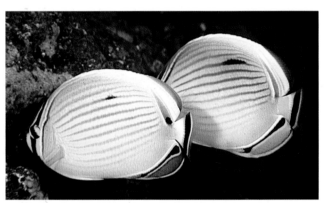

Fig. 1. Swimming as a pair in Bali, Indonesia, *Chaetodon lunulatus* and its Pacific sibling *C. trifasciatus.* Several sibling butterflyfishes overlap in range, but usually form pairs between their own kind. Mixed pairs are rare and may produce infertile offspring.

Siblings are very closely related and always placed in the same genus. Those that share key-characteristics or certain diagnostic features are also closely related and belong to the same genus. When there are a number of similar species in a genus, that derived from a common ancestor, they are referred to as a species-complex. Species that have evolved with other strong features that typify them are usually placed in their own genus, but like species level, the genus level is sometimes difficult to determined with intermediate forms. You can't simply draw a line between levels.

Each species is given a scientific name that consists of two parts, the first is the genus, and the second the species. If a particular genus comprises a number of species, the first or genus name is repeated for each species and followed by a different second or species name. Scientific names are always written in italics. The genera start with a capital letter, while species always start in lower case.

EVOLUTION - SPECIES CREATION

GENERAL

Creatures change over time, but not without reason. In general, each species is perfectly suited to a particular environment, 'in tune' as often stated. In a stable environment there is no need to change and species can remain the same for numerous generations with perhaps some 'finetuning' that may be reflected in slight colour variations or aspects of behaviour that makes life a little easier. When a stable environment is interrupted by some natural cause, such as temperature and/or sea-level alterations, the habitat and its creatures change or move accordingly to suit new conditions. Changes versus time are variable, from gradual over millions of years or relatively fast, taking a few thousand years. The rate of change determines the adaptability of life forms. If changes are gradual, then species can adapt more easily compared to fast rates. Fast changing habitat causes a species dropout, or creates highly adaptable new species. The evolution process is more related to change in the environment than time. Changes may happen regularly or after long stable times and can come in various forms. It could be a single event that could have little to enormous consequences, depending on severity and duration, restabilise, or continue with fluctuations or change at various rates. One could compare a volcanic eruption with an ice age as the opposite extremes: the first being very short but drastic, probably causing a kill, not effecting evolution; the second more gradual and causing slow modifications of faunas where species can adapt. At great depths in the sea, where temperatures and conditions are very stable, fishes are the most primitive and like living fossils. In the shallows, where temperatures and conditions greatly fluctuate, fishes are the most evolved and highly diversified. Continental drift over tens of millions of years, making land rise and sink, shaped the world as we know it. Oceanic currents changed, influencing the weather, altering land and sea environments. Global change continues to occur, seemingly at the same slow pace, and so will evolution.

ADAPTATION

Nature always experiments and offspring receive something extra from their parents, but with many variations distributed throughout their brood. A slightly longer snout or some colour modification in some may give them the edge to survive better than the rest. The survivors will reproduce and maintain the advantage that made them more successful with added variations, amplifying the best features to be more successful with each next generation. Particular features will develop in different habitats, and given enough time such species become so different from their original form, that they are no longer compatible. Species change with the environment, resulting in additional or separate species, and sometimes in a complex of new species between different environments, depending on circumstances.

Humans have created ornamental forms of particular fish-species in relatively short periods by selective breeding over a few hundred years. Naturally (in situ), such changes are much slower, probably taking thousands to millions of years, depending on many factors such as lifespans and environmental changes, or dispersal possibilities during environmental changes. The larger species that usually live much longer than the smaller ones are clearly at a disadvantage by having fewer generations over time. The larger species are less numerous and live in more stable and deeper habitats. The small species are most specious in shallow tropical zones.

FAUNAS DIVIDING

Continental drift causes land to move slowly across the earth surface. Like Noahs Ark, entire faunas, including the surrounding sea, were taken on a journey that began millions of years ago. During that time habitats change in various ways or to degrees, between different areas, regardless of distance or time. Where areas were split, drifting in opposite directions, we can find parallel-zones far apart, in which parts of the faunas changed the least, closely representing the ancestral fauna. Such zones of particular interest, especially when in subtropical waters as found in common between Japan and Australia, indicating an event of a long time ago. Separations of faunas between Indian and Pacific Oceans appear to be relatively recent, and are more related to change of the environment than continental drift. Temperatures and sea-levels fluctuated during ice-ages, causing faunas to slowly shift geographically. The species changed slightly between the different areas, resulting in sub-species and many closely related siblings. Some of the most recent ones have returned to their ancestral ground and can be found together in the areas of Java or Bali, Indonesia. Those dispersing earlier are geographically much further separated, but the siblings remain remarkably similar. Faunas moving and enable to follow the same conditions changed little, but in the area left behind changed, often dramatically. If a species survived in the changed area, it would change accordingly, whilst those migrating away would change only slightly by comparison. The resulting three forms are usually isolated and can be geographical variations, subspecies, or valid species. There are many such examples in the Indo-Pacific: the most changed species in the area of Indonesia, the least changed in two very similar forms, one to the west and the other to the east, north or south.

When a particular species becomes separated into isolated populations, for whatever reason, each with their own environmental pressures, several developments can take place. Firstly, the entire fauna, including plants corals and fish amongst others, gradually travels in a certain direction, staying in touch with conditions that requires the least change. The species are under no pressure to change. When the faunas are split under those conditions, migration is usually in opposite directions and can travel great distance with time, resulting in some very similar species geographically found far apart. Examples can be found between Japan and Australia, and even between the Red Sea and Hawaii. Migration of faunas have occurred over millions of years and still show remarkable similarities in the make up of species between different areas, some of which so similar that many scientists have problems understanding this phenomena. The best approach appears to be to treat an entire fauna as a specific entity. Usually many species show individuality to various degrees, from clearly being good species to those difficult to separate into species in their own right. Techniques of determining a species is generally based on physical features with some limitations and we don't always see differences easily. Modern techniques such as electrophoresis or DNA can be useful, but don't always give results. The lumping of similar forms into single species has the potential of endangering a species. Different looking populations should be treated as separate species until shown *without doubt* to be the same, rather than the other way around. With loss of habitat, especially estuarine ones that are taken over by human development, populations could vanish.

The more species have evolved and are different at higher degrees, the more the above analyses becomes obvious, including at higher taxon levels. In general, the most similar species are the furthest apart, geographically speaking. Secondly, as the fauna changes or migrates away from an area, those left behind, such as in land-locked situations have to adapt and change the most to suit new conditions or vanish. In some cases marine environments were cut-off from the sea and gradually turned into freshwater lakes. Some species were able to adapt, even sharks. Isolation can just as well be in the sea itself. If one imagines a small island with quickly changing conditions and nowhere to go, the only options for species is adapting to changes to survive, or alternatively vanish. In most stable environments of recent times, the species diversity is the greatest, often genera have numerous species. The greatest diversity is found near the largest land masses, but especially where numerous strings of islands form extensions over great distances, such as the Indo-Malay region where island hopping of larval fishes can influence speciation. When speciation occurred earlier in time, the diversity is at different levels now, and this shows in the various eco systems. For instance, in temperate shallow seas diversity shows at genus level, whilst in deep water, with the more primitive fishes, this is at family levels.

When recent separation of faunas occurred, the the different species are most similar. Such species are mainly divided between Indian and Pacific Oceans, the sibling species. In many cases there are colour variations that are seen as geographical forms, and this is particularly relative to Maldives fishes. However, in future I expect that most of such variations will be recognised as species in their own right.

Fig. 2. Left, the Exquisite Wrasse *Cirrhilabrus exquisites* is only found in the Indian Ocean. Right, its Pacific sibling going under the same name, eventhough, it is totally different and should be recognised as a species in its own right. Juveniles and females of sibling wrasses species are often similar, but fully coloured males as shown in these pictures should erase any doubt.

SCIENTIFIC & COMMON NAMES

With many languages and many localised names used for numerous creatures or plants, a scientific framework of taxons to overcome this problem began about 200 years ago. Now we can apply an international name to a fish, the scientific name, so everybody knows what fish we are talking about. Similarly, to a family such as LABRIDAE that represents a particular group of fishes known under various names or in different languages, are known as wrasses in English. Fish taxonomy has some way to go yet to get itself sorted out. On the one hand, we are still finding new species; and on the other hand, the same species may have been given different names by different people. The first name has priority and later names are synonyms. As literature research continues, and original specimens are examined in collections held by institutions, an older name than the presently used one may be found, and changed accordingly. Sometimes species placed in different genera are found to be generically the same, so the oldest genus is recognised. This may cause a minor change to the actual species name. The genus has a certain gender that can be feminine, masculine or neutral, and this is reflected in the species name as well. Masculine names of species often end in -us- and equivalent feminine names ends in -a-. As the various revisions or studies iron out problems, scientific names remain unstable among some groups. Not everybody agrees to what is a species. Usually someone who specialises in a particular group will find some differences, but often is biased towards wanting to finding this. Some scientists are determined in calling something a new species, going to great length to point out minor differences, whilst others lump different ones together, only pointing out the similarities. In the process of producing this book, several species received name changes, and even some genera among gobies were changed at the last minute. Several species names are questionable and marked as such. When a species is unknown, it is abbreviated as sp.

Several species are abbreviated as spp.

Common names used in the Maldives are a combination of local and introduced names from visitors from all parts of the globe. The common name in English in this book doesn't necessarily represent the local name, but one that is more suitable to most visitor-divers. However, alternative names are included. Most countries use similar names, except Americans who often mix-up similar families, or combine scientific names with common names. Eventhough, the information world is shrinking at a fast rate, names will always remain a point of discussion. Fishermen use different names from aquarists and divers often have yet another version. Fisheries departments will claim that theirs is the 'official' one, but again that remains debatable as these market names are often wrong from an international point of view. For this book I have used names preferred by divers or aquarists, or relevant to the particular species itself.

ABOUT FISHES

Whilst we can admire beautifully coloured fishes, there is much to learn about their behaviour. Divers are in the unique position to see and observe fishes naturally and have discovered many interesting aspects about the way they live. Before the diving era, much of what was known about fishes was based on speculation and studies in aquariums. Seeing behaviour first hand often contradicts with what is documented. This doesn't mean that documents are wrong, but more likely is caused by species behaving differently in other areas. Scientific studies on fish behaviour in the wild have been limited and are often narrowly focussed to particular species or certain aspects of behaviour. Documenting behaviour in words is very limited in bringing the message across and can easily be wrongly interpreted. A good photograph can show much more and requires a simple caption to be understood. Scientific papers are usually produced by someone who is an expert on the subject, and to fully understand such documents, one has to be reasonably familiar or an expert on a similar level. If not, such papers can be dangerous grounds if taken out of context. Generalisation on aspects of behaviour is particularly dangerous, even when dealing with a single species. For instance: many butterflyfish occur in pairs in certain areas and it is often assumed that this is the case everywhere else, but such fishes can school in other areas. This can relate directly to differences in habitat and competition. Keeping an open mind is most important, and expect the unexpected when visiting new areas.

Many fishes behave differently in the Maldives from their counterparts in mainland waters. They behave more like oceanic species, as around Pacific islands, by the tendency to school compared to pairing by many identical species in continental waters. Some, that elsewhere are shallow water species, live only deep in the Maldives that is a direct reflection of food availability, and not related to temperature as often suggested. Studying fish behaviour is not only fascinating, but always something new comes along and makes you want to know more. However, one has to be very careful in observations as we are influenced by what we read, and can easily make the wrong assumption. Such an example I saw published, was a group of *Thalassoma* wrasses robbing the eggs from an *Abudefduf* (Sergeant Major) nesting site, with the caption stating that these fish were spawning! *Thalassoma* wrasses are pelagic spawners and their eggs float away in tidal currents.

COLOUR AND CAMOUFLAGE

Many reef fishes have amazing colours and bolt patterns, but these are all for a particular purpose. They can serve for recognition, warning, display or confuse a potential predator. Juveniles are inexperienced and most vulnerable, a stage in which the process of learning to survive is most important, and depend on appearance. They usually have colours that are more suitable to avoid detection, confuse or put a predator off. Many species go through various colour changes with growth. Sexes are often different, especially in territorial species that live in groups with dominating males. Colour patterns often serve to break-up the body outline with stripes or bands. Some important parts such as eyes are often coloured the same as the immediate areas around them, whilst one or more eye-like spots or false-eyes (called ocellus, single, and ocelli, plural) somewhere else on the body confuses a predator. The real eye is camouflaged and protected, whilst a predator striking expect it to swim in another direction. Small juveniles often have several ocelli and may appear as a face of a much larger fish, when view side-on.

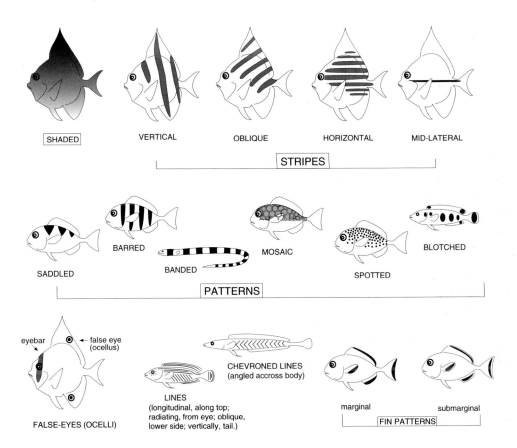

Fig. 3. COLOUR PATTERNS

Most fishes are camouflaged in one way or another; small fishes to escape detection by predators, and the predators to get close to prey. Open water fishes are usually silvery, shaded with bluish or greenish backs that reflect their surroundings whilst reef fishes are coloured to suit their surroundings and habits. Slow fishes that live in direct contact with the bottom are best camouflaged, those on sand matching the texture and colour, and those on reef the various features combining colour and shape. A flounder on the sand is rarely seen unless it moves, like the stonefish on the reef that is almost impossible to detect. Fishes that are more mobile make use of coverage of reefs and use camouflage to lesser extent, but some of the colours we see in photographs that are bright can be for camouflage. Bright red fishes that live deep or active at night are actually camouflaged because red light doesn't travel far, red is like having no colour at all in natural light at depth.

MIMICRY

MIMICRY, meaning imitating or copying, is commonly used by fishes in various forms, some of which have evolved to amazing perfection. One of the best examples is the Mimic Filefish *Paraluteres prionurus* that is the perfect copy of the poisonous Saddled Pufferfish *Canthigaster valentini,* usually avoided by predators. Producing poison to the system requires energy and special diet, thus is expensive, but the Filefish gets around as easily by bluff as the pufferfish. They are so similar, that only a close look reveals the long dorsal and anal fin bases compared to the short ones of the pufferfish. Several similar examples are among blennies, a harmless species looking like one with a venomous bite, and several other fish species taking on similar colours as juvenile until outgrowing its model.

Fig. 5.
Left, Saddled Pufferfish *Canthigaster valentini* and right, Mimic Filefish *Paraluteres prionurus.*

Fishes learn quickly, especially when food is involved, and already know the easy pickings around divers. Over time, evolution has created some amazing examples, especially the cunning False Cleanerfish *Aspidontus taeniatus,* a blenny and a near perfect copy of the Cleaner Wrasse *Labroides dimidiatus.* Whilst the wrasse removes small parasite, the blenny will bite and remove skin or fin bits instead. Some small blennies mix with schooling planktivores and bite unexpectedly at fish swimming past. Many predators have become very cunning in capturing prey by using a disguise, ambush, or following others for an easy meal. Some small groupers try to look like wrasses or damsels of the same size that feed on small invertebrates, enabling them to get close enough to snap up unsuspected juveniles damselfishes.

Often small juveniles mimic uninteresting things, like a leaf floating on the surface or along the bottom in currents, that are of no interest to predators. Others mimic something bad-tasting or poisonous, such as a flatworm and nudibranch, that bare bright warning colours. In addition, by swimming or moving in certain ways, nature's copies can be very convincing. Tiny post-larvae batfish are an excellent example of mimicking a leaf and when approached will flatten itself against the surface. Tiny juvenile anglerfish sit openly on rocks, pretending to be a nudibranch and several small soles mimic flatworms on sand.

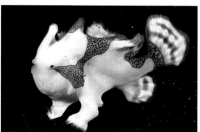

Fig. 6.
A juvenile Clown Anglerfish *Antennarius maculatus* photographed in Bali, Indonesia. They are typically brightly coloured and sit openly in coralline-algae reef, pretending to be a nudibranch.

CLEANING STATIONS

Specialisation of fishes is evident in various ways, usually in regards to feeding, but generally is reflected in morphological features, such as a very long nose, numerous gill rakers, large mouth, etc. A different form of specialisation has developed into a relationship between fishes themselves, helping each other by favours and rewards, whereby small fishes help the usually large ones getting rid of external parasites in return for food. The parasites are part of the diet for the small fishes, and in addition feed on food-bits stuck between teeth or filtering parts in the gills. A few fishes have almost exclusively adapted to such activities and are called cleanerfishes. The most famous of all is the Cleaner Wrasse *Labroides dimidiatus.* Cleaning activities begin from the post-larval stage and tiny juveniles are found in small caves or below overhangs of reef. Adults usually work in pairs, and found in a particular place on the reef that has prominent features such as a particular cave or bommie. Such places are known as cleaning stations and visited by reef fishes as well as pelagics that come to be served at a particular time of the day. Shrimps often work together with these fishes, as they too have adapted to this behaviour in the specially established spots. The busy times are late afternoon and fishes may actually form a queue, waiting patiently for their turn. When inspected, most fishes change colour that assists in showing their problem. Parasites usually match the colour of their host, but when the host changes colour it has trouble catching-up, and the host paling its colour makes the parasite readily visible. Assistance is also by opening the mouth and gills for easy access to the cleaners. Cleaning behaviour is done by numerous fishes, sometimes juveniles only, but often is a localised behaviour. In some areas certain butterflyfishes are active cleaners and sometimes schooling bannerfishes clean large pelagic species.

Fig. 7.
Surgeonfish *Acanthurus thompsoni* in a cleaning station with the Cleaner Wrasse *Labroides dimidiatus,* and participating is a juvenile Diana Wrasse *Bodianus diana*, that commonly cleans when young.

SYMBIOTIC RELATIONSHIPS

When different life forms live together in a mutual dependant relation- or partnership, it is called symbiosis. Well known are the anemone fishes, a damselfish that lives amongst the stinging tentacles of some large anemones. The anemone accepts these fishes as being part of itself, the mucus on the fish containing a compound obtained from the anemone itself, probably by rubbing all external parts against the anemone's non-stinging underside. The fish is protected from predators amongst the stinging tentacles, and in return the anemone is guarded by the fish from those that would like to eat it, such as butterflyfishes. In addition the anemone can position itself in current-prone positions and feed during the day, as well as at night. Most other anemones are nocturnal and live in reef or under sand during the day. In the Maldives there is a single genus of anemonefish but several anemone genera. Some other fishes occur intermittently in these anemones, juvenile Three-spot Humbugs *Dascyllus trimaculatus* and small wrasses swim sometimes between long tentacles. In addition some interesting crabs and shrimps share the anemones.

Fig. 8. Blackfoot Anemonefish *Amphiprion nigripes* in the tentacles of an anemone.

The other group commonly observed in partnerships are the shrimpgobies. This is a large group with several genera and many species, that live with Snapping Shrimps, *Alpheus* spp. The shrimps are excellent burrowers and make tunnels that serve the gobies as homes. The gobies stand guard at the entrances, signalling the shrimps if safe to come out or not. Sometimes a goby guides the poor-sighted shrimp from the hole, the shrimp staying in touch with the long feelers. Adult gobies usually live in pairs, together with a pair of adult shrimps. Juvenile gobies normally live with juvenile shrimps, both small, but occasionally odd sized couples can be found.

Fig. 9. Dracula Shrimp *Stonogobiops dracula* lives with the snapper shrimp *Alpheus randalli*.

SPAWNING & PARENTAL CARE

Most of Maldives larger reef fishes are pelagic spawners, in which males and female release eggs and sperm simultaneously in surface waters. These include the major families such as wrasses, surgeons, parrots, butterflies and angelfishes, amongst many others. Eggs are usually tiny and weightless but in some cases, such as with halfbeaks, spawning is over seagrass beds where the eggs sink and stick to the seagrass leaves. Most of these fishes produce millions of eggs, depending on their size as most eggs are between 0.5 and 1 mm in diameter. Some families such as damsels and triggerfishes deposit eggs on the bottom that hatch after a relatively short period and produce pelagic larval fishes. The most advanced are the pipefishes that produce well developed young with a short pelagic stage. Fishes that take care of the eggs produce much less numerous broods but much larger eggs, as their survival rate is increased dramatically.

Fishes that have no pelagic stage are not known from the Maldives. Most spawning activities are on the largest tides in phase with the moon cycle, usually near full moon. Wrasses, parrotfishes and surgeonfishes are usually active during this period on dusk, congregating in reef channels where strong currents are favourable to take the eggs as far away as possible from the reef. Eventually, the developing larvae are carried back and post-larvae settle on the various habitats on the reefs. Damselfishes lay their eggs exposed on reefs, where they can easily be seen, but are heavily guarded by the parents. The various groups within the families use different strategies. The sergeant majors are community spawners, where a school forms individual pairs and lay the eggs in patches close to each other. The anemonefishes deposit their eggs on a solid object immediately next to the anemone. Some others clear a patch of live coral tissue to lay their eggs on its skeleton. Most gobies and some other small reef dwellers have eggs hidden in the reefs or under rocks. Large male triggerfishes prepare nesting sites on deep sand or reef flats. After eggs are laid, the sites are vigorously defended by both sexes for the few days the eggs take to hatch. The male Titan Triggerfish will readily charge at a diver that ventures into the territory, and can give a painful bite or just a full speed hit with the mouth that is as bad.

Fig. 10.
Blackfoot Anemonefish *Amphiprion nigripes* protecting its eggs, attached to the coral-rock next to the anemone.

Cardinalfishes are mouth brooders, in which the male incubates the eggs in the mouth after spawning (see Page 80). The egg mass is large and the extended mouth readily visible. The brood is regularly moved to provide oxygen, almost in a rough way, spitting them partly out of the mouth and back, probably to get rid of bad eggs. Many species school, and young hatch simultaneously from numerous parents at the top of large tides.

DEVELOPMENT & AGE

Pelagic eggs hatch quickly and most larvae measure a few mm long, generally just over double the egg diameter, bursting out from the crammed egg, less than one mm in diameter. Diet comprises phytoplankton and the growth rate is quick. Most species reaching one or two cm in a few weeks before settling on reefs, but some grow much larger, size depending on the family. Surgeonfishes can reach 5 cm before settling. The more developed larvae, that hatch from those species with parental care, are born large and have a much shorter pelagic stage before settling on the bottom. Larval pipefishes are often 3 or 4 cm long when settling. Most larvae are transparent, showing few melanophores. Fishes settling on the substrate following a larval stage, called post-larvae, quickly colour up, change shape and become juveniles that are more recognisable as a species. Most juveniles grow quickly in the first few weeks, usually doubling their length or more. Small species can mature in a few months but large species may take a number of years to reach full adult size. This only applies to shallow water species that are included in this book. Fishes living in very deep water, 1000 m or more, can be small and very old (100+ years) at the same time.

Habitat requirements often change with growth and development of a species. The colouration of reef fishes can change dramatically at different stages. The colour pattern of a small juvenile that is often bolt, would be unsuitable at a large size, drawing unwanted attention. Changes with growth can be gradual or in stages, depending on the species and circumstances. When mimicry is involved, the mimic often outgrows the model and quickly changes when reaching that size, sometimes not just changing colours, but also morphological features. With most fishes the changes are gradual to suit the environment, but when moving to other habitats the colour may need matching straight away. Some fishes are capable of changing almost instantly, especially those that rely on camouflage for protection.

The age of fishes varies greatly with size and depths. Most reef fishes live from one year to several decades. Ghostpipefishes are thought to live annually. Some dartgobies *Ptereleotris* lived about ten year in an aquarium and large *Pomacentrus* angelfishes have been kept over 20 years. Deep water fishes get much older, some only 50 cm long living in about 1000 m depth were aged to 160 years old.

MEASUREMENTS

FIN HEIGHT

BODY DEPTH

HEAD LENGTH

BASE LENGTH

FIN LENGTH

TOTAL LENGTH

BODY WIDTH

EXTERNAL FEATURES

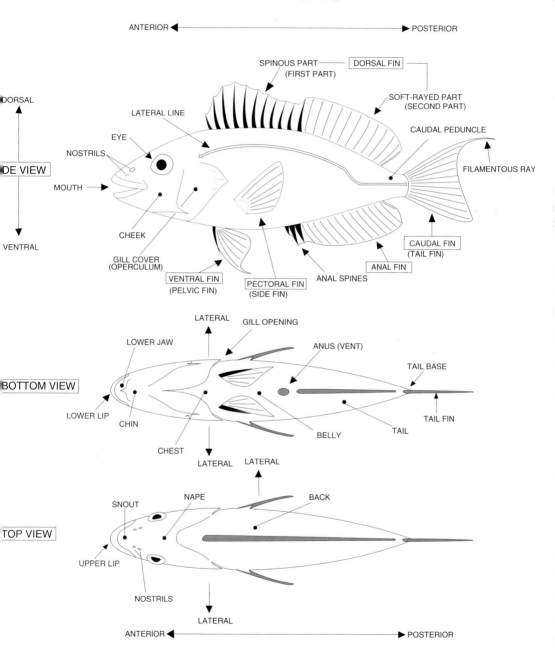

ANTERIOR ◄──────────────────────────────► POSTERIOR

SPINOUS PART — DORSAL FIN
(FIRST PART)

SOFT-RAYED PART
(SECOND PART)

CAUDAL PEDUNCLE

DORSAL

LATERAL LINE

EYE

NOSTRILS

DE VIEW

FILAMENTOUS RAY

MOUTH

VENTRAL

CHEEK

GILL COVER
(OPERCULUM)

CAUDAL FIN
(TAIL FIN)

VENTRAL FIN
(PELVIC FIN)

PECTORAL FIN
(SIDE FIN)

ANAL SPINES

ANAL FIN

LATERAL

GILL OPENING

LOWER JAW

ANUS (VENT)

TAIL BASE

BOTTOM VIEW

LOWER LIP

CHIN

TAIL FIN

CHEST

BELLY

TAIL

LATERAL

LATERAL

SNOUT

NAPE

BACK

TOP VIEW

UPPER LIP

NOSTRILS

LATERAL

ANTERIOR ◄──────────────────────────────► POSTERIOR

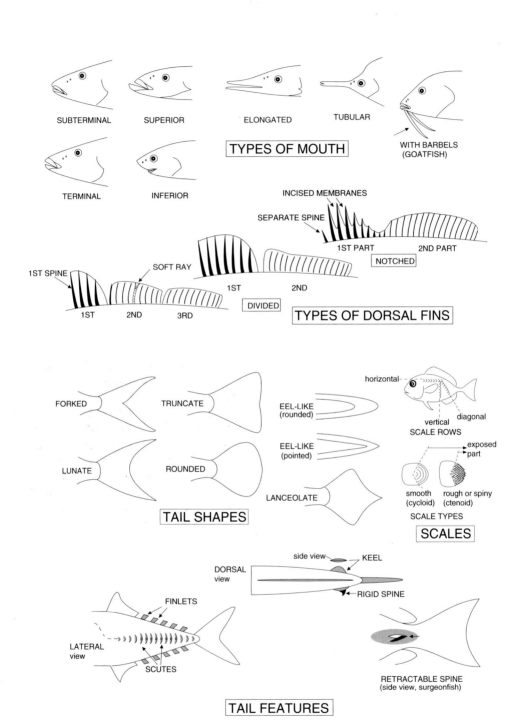

SUBTERMINAL   SUPERIOR   ELONGATED   TUBULAR

TYPES OF MOUTH

WITH BARBELS
(GOATFISH)

TERMINAL   INFERIOR

INCISED MEMBRANES

SEPARATE SPINE

1ST PART   2ND PART

NOTCHED

1ST SPINE

SOFT RAY

1ST   2ND

DIVIDED

1ST   2ND   3RD

TYPES OF DORSAL FINS

FORKED   TRUNCATE   EEL-LIKE
(rounded)

horizontal

vertical   diagonal
SCALE ROWS

exposed
part

LUNATE   ROUNDED   EEL-LIKE
(pointed)

smooth   rough or spiny
(cycloid)   (ctenoid)

LANCEOLATE

SCALE TYPES

TAIL SHAPES

SCALES

side view   KEEL

DORSAL
view

RIGID SPINE

FINLETS

LATERAL
view

SCUTES

RETRACTABLE SPINE
(side view, surgeonfish)

TAIL FEATURES

22

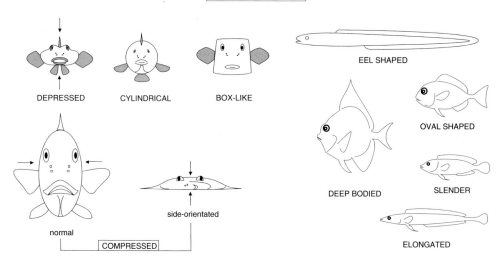

DEPRESSED   CYLINDRICAL   BOX-LIKE

EEL SHAPED

OVAL SHAPED

DEEP BODIED   SLENDER

normal

side-orientated

COMPRESSED

ELONGATED

SHAPES OF FISHES

Most people are familiar with fishes caught on a line and know the shape of an eel. The seahorse is not often recognised as a fish and represents one of the more unusually shaped types. Fish fill every niche of the aquatic habitat, like birds on the land, that require colour, size and shape to suit. Reef or sand dwellers, the pelagics, hunters and graziers have different needs and adapted accordingly, readily noticed by shape. Fast fishes need to be streamlined, those living on the bottom and don't need to move can be shaped like a rock or a stick. Most fishes we see swimming around the reef, the groupers, damsels, fusiliers snappers etc, are perch-like in shape and fin features, however each group varies in varies ways. Some are short, other long, thick or thin, as shown above with the appropriate terms that are generally used. Some fishes have adapted to living in a different way to most, like the flatfishes that lay on their sides, or seahorses, ghostpipefishes and shrimpfishes have a vertical composure. So flatfishes are compressed and not depressed, and those fishes swimming vertical are slender and not deep bodied.

MORAY EELS - MURAENIDAE

A large family of eels with at least 10 genera and an estimated 170 species occur worldwide, over 200 according to some authors. About 40 species have been recorded from the Maldives but the majority are very secretive and are rarely seen when diving, living inside the reef or in holes in sand. Only a few species are common on reefs, and these are usually seen during the day with just their head visible from holes. Some species come out at night, openly hunting over reefs and sand bottoms. Morays are carnivores that take a mixture of invertebrates whole, such as shrimps, octopus and fishes, including smaller eels. Their body is nearly all muscle and they are extremely strong, and combined with powerful jaws they can attack larger creatures or join in mauling activities by others, ripping pieces away by twisting their bodies. Some species are capable to knot their body for leverage. Normally eels are shy but may get used to divers. Large individuals can be several metres long and have the potential to do a lot of damage. Feeding these creatures in some areas has led to divers in hospital and should not be encouraged.

Morays in Malé Harbour.

Black Cheek Moray *Gymnothorax breedeni*

The distinctive black patch mark below the eye easily identifies this species. It is common on reef walls and steep slopes with holes to depths of about 20 m, usually only the head is visible. Territorial species and can be aggressive towards divers, will bite if provoked. Widespread Indian Ocean, ranging to some oceanic locations in the Pacific.
Length to 65 cm.

Honeycomb Moray *Gymnothorax favagineus*

A basically white species with black blotches with interspaces forming a honeycomb pattern. The size of the blotches is variable between individuals and size, often in relation to habitat. Those living on clear coral reefs usually have proportionally less black than those found in turbid waters. Observed to depth of 45 m, but also as shallow as 6 m. Widespread Indo-Pacific. One of the largest morays, to about 2 m long.
Photo left: Mustag Hussain; right: Scott Michael.

White-mouth Moray *Gymnothorax meleagris*

A common species but prefers very shallow depth and juveniles often in tidal zones. In corals or rubble on reef flats and in harbours. Mouth white inside, contrasting the outer dark skin with small white spots. Widespread Indo-Pacific. Length to 60 cm.
Photo: Indonesia.

Yellow-mouth Moray *Gymnothorax nudivomer*

Inner and outer reef slopes, usually in depth of 30+ m in the Maldives. White-spotted, sometimes reticulated patterns. Best identified from similar species by the yellow inside the mouth. Widespread Indo-Pacific. Reported to 1 m length.
Photo: Jörg Aebi.

Giant Moray *Gymnothorax javanicus*

The largest known Indo-Pacific moray. Best distinguished from similar species by the numerous small dark spots on top of the head and back. Lives in various reef habitats from intertidal to about 50 m depth. A widespread species and often common.
Reported to a length of 2.4 m and a weight of just over 30 kg.
Photo of large individual with cleaner wrasses: Mustag Hussain.

Yellow-margin Moray
Gymnothorax flavimarginatus

Similar to Giant Moray but has a mottle pattern and large individuals have a purplish grey snout. Small juveniles sometimes yellow with brown mottling. Various reef habitats but prefers clear coastal reefs and not common in the Maldives. Widespread Indo-Pacific. Length to 1.2 m.
Photo: Flores, Indonesia.

Albino Moray *Gymnothorax* sp.

This large, 1 m, individual was photographed at South Malé Atoll in 32 m depth. It appears to be very similar to *G. javanicus*, except for colour and is possibly an albino form. However, alternativily could represent a new species.
Photo: Jörg Aebi.

Little Moray
Gymnothorax richardsoni

A small species that lives in shallow rubble lagoons and coastal reef flats, often found under large loose dead coral pieces to depths of about 10 m. Identified by the dense starry pattern in an indistinctive dark banding along most of the body. Widespread Indo-Pacific. Length to 30 cm.
Photo: Bali, Indonesia.

Bar-tail Moray *Gymnothorax zonipectis*

Various habitats from shallow reefs with dense coral growth to deep in clear lagoon reef formations. Sometimes in deep caves along drop-offs. Secretive amongst corals or in reef during the day, sometimes out in the open at night. Widespread Indo-Pacific. Reported length to 45 cm, usually to about 30 cm.
Photo: Flores, Indonesia.

Spot-face Moray *Gymnothorax fimbriatus*

A pale species with small black spots on the face when adult, proportionally much larger in young. Prefers protected inshore waters among dead corals, common in harbours and in small caves on slopes to about 45 m depth. Reported length to 80 cm. Largest seen in Malé harbour, in photograph, about 65 cm.
Photo, juvenile with shrimp: Bali, Indonesia.

Undulate Moray *Gymnothorax undulatus*

Common in the Maldives but usually only seen at night when it hunts fishes that sleep in crevices in reefs. Can be aggressive towards divers. Protected reefs and lagoons to about 20 m depth in the Maldives. Widespread Indo-Pacific. Snout often yellow.
Length to at least 1 m.
Photo: Out at night, hunting and seeking out small fishes in holes, by Toshikazu Kozawa.

Y-patterned Moray *Gymnothorax berndti*

A rare but very distinctive species with a pale grey colour with y-patterns along entire body. Prefers rock and sponge habitat, usually over 30 m depth. Originally described from Japan, also known from Taiwan and Hawaii.
Length to 1 m.
Photo: aquarium, Japan.

Zebra Moray *Gymnomuraena zebra*

Easily recognised by the close set narrow dark bands. Very secretive and shy, even at night it quickly retreats out of sight. Shallow reef flats and slopes to 50 m depth, occasionally found in pairs. Widespread Indo-Pacific. Length to 1 m. Photo right: Charles Anderson; left: Aquarium photo, Australia.

Barred Moray *Echidna polyzona*

Distinctive banded pattern only in juveniles, gradually breaking up in to blotched pattern. Various shallow reef habitat, usually coastal and more silty zones, but secretive during the day and not often seen. Mainly out at night in search of crabs and shrimps. Widespread Indo-Pacific.
Length to 60 cm.

Clouded Moray *Echidna nebulosa*

A common shallow water species in protected areas such as harbours. Usually amongst dead coral rubble pieces. Sometimes hunting for crabs during the day in seagrass and rubble mixed habitats. Usually in depths less than 10 m. Has a distinctive starry pattern along the body, forming series of dark blotches with some yellow spots. Widespread Indo-Pacific.
Length to 60 cm.

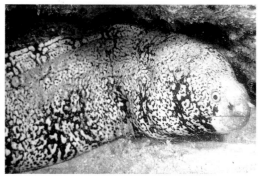

Peppered Moray *Siderea picta*

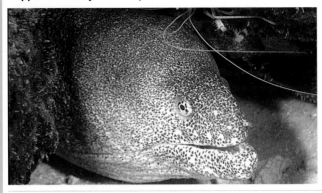

A common eel that prefers silty reefs. Often just below the intertidal zone, found in dead reefs in holes or where rubble pieces are piled up below jetties. They feed primarily on crabs and have been seen leaping at crabs just above the water line. Recognised by the pale grey to white colour and fine dark spotting. Widespread Indo-Pacific.
Length to 1 m.

White-eyed Moray *Siderea thyrsoidea*

A common Maldives species, especially in silty harbours, but also can be found deep and often on shipwrecks in coastal waters to depths of about 35 m. Sometimes several living together or mixed with other species. Easily recognised by the bright white colour in the eyes. Widespread Indo-Pacific.
Length to 65 cm.

Ribbon Eel *Rhimomuraena quaesita*

Readily identified by their unusual shape and colour. Uncommon in most of the Maldives. Only known to dive-guides in a few localities. Lives in mixed sand and reef habitat and usually seen with just the head exposed. Waving a fingers at safe distance in front of the head may draw them from out further. They seem to have a poor eye-sight and rely on smell and sensing pressure changes to catch prey, usually small fishes such as damsels. Occurs on reef crests and slopes from 3 to at least 40 m depth. Length to 1.2 m.

Photos left: Female showing signs of black colour fading and photographed several months later when change to blue phase. Ripe females are thought to turn all yellow but are rarely seen. Photos: Jörg Aebi.
Below left: Female swimming on sand slope during the day. Occasionally they swim from one burrow to another. Bali, Indonesia.
Below right: Blue male, usually larger and more commonly observed than female. Photo: Jörg Aebi.

SNAKE & WORM EELS - OPHICHTHIDAE

A very large and diverse family, dividable in several sub-families, with some 50 genera and 250+ species worldwide, but comparatively few are seen by divers. Most live completely buried in sand or mud and few species just show their head. About 15 species are know from the Maldives but no doubt many more will be discovered as time goes by. Several of the photographs included here are new records for the Maldives. In these eels the eyes are placed about centraly above the mouth. They typically are very long and often have a bony tail end that enable them to quickly bury backwards into the bottom. Some species are small and look more like worms than fish, and others are snake like. Some actually mimic banded seasnakes and moves about openly during the day in lagoons and over shallow reef flats. Diet comprises fish and invertebrates such as octopus and shrimps. In Australia, a snake-eel was observed eating a snapping shrimp.

Napoleon Eel *Ophichthys bonaparta*

A very distinctive species by its colour pattern on the head and body, however, latter rarely seen unless it is caught. Its body is broadly banded in contrast to the unusual blotches on the head. Various sand and rubble habitats from shallow lagoons to deep sand flats. Typically seen as shown in photograph. Widespread Indo-Pacific.
Length to 75 cm.

Crocodile Eel *Brachysomophis crocodilinus*

The eyes on this species are placed far forward over the very long jaws, near the tip of the snout, giving it the unusual look. Not commonly observed and only known from few sightings throughout the Indo-Pacific. With only the head exposed from the sand, matching the colours of the surroundings, it is easily overlooked.
Length to 1 m.
Photo: Scott Michael, Indonesia.

Black-pitted Sand-Eel *Pisonophis cancrivorus*

The pores on the head are black and usually stand out when the eel is brown. It varies in colour according to habitat but Maldives specimens that live in the normally very pale coloured sand are pale accordingly. It is usually seen with just the snout and eyes above the bottom with the rest of the body vertically down. Widespread Indo-Pacific.
Length to 75 cm.
Photo below: Mabul, Malaysia.

Marbled Snake-Eel *Callechelys marmorata*

A variable species, from plain sandy colour to dense black mottling on the head, usually the only part visible. Like most sand eels, little is known about their behaviour. It is found on sand flats from 5 to 30 m, and widespread Indo-Pacific and ranges into warm-temperate zones.
Length to 60 cm.
Photo, dark form: Flores, Indonesia.

Banded Snake-Eel *Myrichthys colubrinus*

Generally the only sand eel observed by snorkelers, is often mistaken for a sea snake. As a mimic of a highly venomous creature, it shows little fear and goes about hunting for small fishes in holes and crevices during daytime. In Japan this eel species was seen eaten by the seasnake it copies. Shallow protected bays and lagoons. Widespread Indo-Pacific, some geographical variations in the depth of the bands encircling the body or not. Length to almost 1 m.
Photo: Flores, Indonesia, large individual hunting on shallow reef flat during the day.

Spotted Snake-Eel *Myrichthys maculosus*

White to yellowish with rounded black blotches, some spot size variation between light and dark habitats. A nocturnal species that hunts mainly on shallow reef flats but ranges to depths of about 30 m. Often in silty coastal habitat. Widespread Indo-Pacific.
Length to almost 1 m.
Photos: Bali, Indonesia. Large individual hunting on rubble slope at night.

GARDEN EELS - CONGRIDAE

Best known in this family are the garden eels, placed in the sub-family HETEROCONGRINAE. The other subfamily group: congers, the deep water members, are not included here. Garden Eels often form large colonies on sand flats that suggested their common name. They rise vertically out of the sand, to about halfway their length, to feed on plankton. The exact number of species is unknown and several species were only recently discovered. At least three species occur in the Maldives.

Spaghetti Eel
Gorgasia maculata

Congregates in great numbers on sand flats or gentle slopes in depths of 30+ m, especially in current-prone places. Common in the Maldives. Extend themselves a long way out of the sand without leaving the bottom to grab plankton drifting past in currents. Probably restricted to Indian Ocean, several similar species elsewhere.
Length to 70 cm, body depth about 6 mm.

Spotted Garden Eel
Heteroconger hassi

A common species found in most sand habitats, from shallow to deep water flats or gentle slopes, especially in current-prone areas where often in large colonies. Easily recognised by the two large black spots on their sides. Widespread Indo-Pacific.
Length to 40 cm.

Splendid Garden Eel
Gorgasia preclara

Found singly or small spread out colonies in current areas. A deep water species rarely seen by divers, usually in 30+ m depth. Identified by orange colour that may appear grey at depth, and large pale spots. Seems to be widespread Indo-Pacific.
Length to 40 cm.
Photo: Roger Steene, Bali, Indonesia..

HERRINGS - CLUPEIDAE

A very large family of mostly small fishes, with about 65 genera and 180 species globally. The largest live in temperate seas and commercially fished for, but tropical species are considered baitfish. They feed on zooplankton. The small species are almost impossible to identify in the wild. Only one species occurs in great numbers in the Maldives, and is included here.

Gold-spot Herring *Herklotsichthys quadrimaculatus*

The large dense schools are often evident from the surface, looking like a single dark mass suspended just away from the waters edge along the beach. In the Maldives, usually a Heron is nearby patrolling the beach for an easy feed. This species is widespread Indo-Pacific.
Length to 15 cm.

HARDYHEADS - ATHERINIDAE

A large family of small silvery fishes with about 29 genera and 150+ species. Mainly coastal species, often in estuaries and some entering freshwater. Only three species are recorded from the Maldives, two of which commonly seen along beaches. They are planktivores and hunted by semi-pelagic species such as immature trevallies or jacks, and often targeted by sea birds.

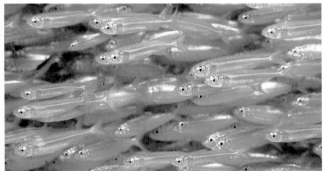

Robust Hardyhead
Atherinomorus lacunosus

Commonly swims along beaches with Gold-spot Herrings, often mixing in the schools. It is less reflective than other species and scales over the back are outlined by dark edges. Widespread Indo-Pacific.
Length to 13 cm.

Silver Hardyhead
Hypoatherina barnesi

Swims with herrings but forms own dense schools, swimming just outside the herring schools and usually closer to the surface. Silvery, reflective species. Widespread Indo-Pacific.
Length to 10 cm.

HALFBEAKS - HEMIRAMPHIDAE

A family of surface fishes with about 12 genera and 80 species worldwide, five of which reported from the Maldives. Elsewhere, also known as garfish. They are primarily tropical marine that school in coastal waters, estuaries, and some have adapted to freshwater. Their lower jaw is greatly extended. Diet comprises algae, plankton and insects that are taken on or near the surface. Two species are commonly seen in the Maldives and included here.

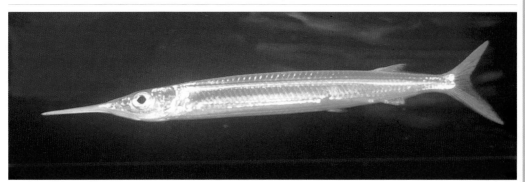

Dussumier's Halfbeak *Hyporhamphus dussumieri*

Greenish or bluish silvery, tail fin rather large. Forms schools over seagrass beds in clear water lagoons. Spawns above the seagrasses and the sticky eggs sink amongst it. Widespread Indo-Pacific.
Length to 25 cm.
Photo: Toshikazu Kozawa.

Reef Halfbeak *Hyporhamphus affinis*

Bluish silvery, rather slender and tail fin not particularly large. Forms schools over sand flats behind reefs or along beaches. Widespread Indo-Pacific, mainly oceanic islands. Length to 25 cm.

NEEDLEFISHES - BELONIDAE

A family of surface fishes with about 10 genera and 30 species worldwide, of which 5 in 4 genera are reported from the Maldives, sometimes called longtoms or seagars. Silvery reflective elongated fishes, the greatly extended jaws with numerous slender teeth. Jaws are proportionally shorter in small young, but this is the opposite in semi-adults. Longtoms swim just below the surface and hunt small surface fishes, in turn they are hunted by large pelagics like tuna, and leap into the air to escape, often skipping along on their tail, seemingly running on the surface. The large species often hunt solitary and some small species form schools. Three species are commonly seen and included here.

Schooling Needlefish *Platybelone argalus*

Often congregates in large schools just below the surface in sheltered parts of reef adjacent to deep current channels. Widespread Indo-Pacific, subspecies in Red Sea and Atlantic.
Length to 45 cm.

Slender Needlefish *Strongylura leiura*

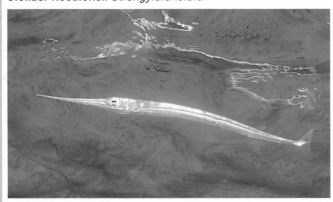

A common slender species with very long jaws. Usually seen singly or a few together that swim apart but within each others visible range, having some cunning hunting tactics. Patrols along beaches where often small herring and hardyheads congregate. Widespread Indo-Pacific.
Length to about 70 cm, including the long elongated jaws.

Crocodile Needlefish *Tylosurus crocodilus*

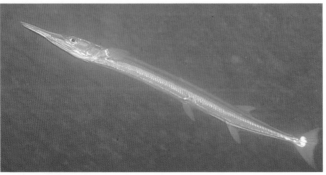

Adults are easily recognised by their large size, and proportionally short snout, but the length of the snout varies with growth and can be relatively long in half-grown individuals. Large individuals are usually seen swimming solitary, adjacent to shores over sand or reef. Wide ranging in all tropical seas, comprising a number of subspecies.
Length to 1.3 m.

EELTAIL CATFISHES - PLOTOSIDAE

Eeltail Catfishes belong to a very large group of mainly freshwater fishes, comprising about 25 families globally. The family PLOTOSIDAE comprises 8 genera, but only one species is commonly seen by divers in tropical waters of the Indo-Pacific, including the Maldives. Catfishes have venomous spines in the fins that can inflict painful wound and repeated stings can be fatal. This groups has an eel-like tail, compared to forked in most other catfish families.

Striped Catfish *Plotosus lineatus*

This species prefers coastal silty conditions and is rarely seen on coral reefs. In the Maldives it is found in silty enclosed harbours where seasonally juveniles swim in dense formations, looking like a single dark body changing shape. Juveniles feed from the bottom surface on detritus. Adults are more solitary and found mainly in ledges during the day, feeding at night and are scavengers.
Length to 25 cm.
Photo, semi-adults: Seychelles, John E. Randall.

LINGS - OPHIDIIDAE

A very large family with some 50 genera and over 150 species globally. Highly diverse and most are found in deep and temperate seas. Only one species is regularly seen by divers in the Maldives.

Bearded Rockling *Brotula multibarbata*

This multi-barbel species is usually mistaken for a catfish. It hunts at night for sleeping fishes and various mobile invertebrates. Retreats quickly into crevices in reefs when caught in light, and swims backwards as fast as forward. Occurs on coastal coral reef slopes, usually in 10+ m depth
Length to 60 cm, usually seen to about 40 cm.
Photo: Izu, Japan.

ANGLERFISHES - ANTENNARIIDAE

A large family of specialised fishes in 12 genera and 41 species known worldwide. Most are found in continental waters and six species are reported from the Maldives. They are not only cryptic, but masters of camouflage, looking like a sponge or some other part of the reef. Juveniles of some species, on the other hand, can be brightly colour, apparently mimicking bad tasting slugs (nudibranchs) or flatworms. Anglerfishes attract their prey with a bait, or luring apparatus, that is dangled in various ways above their large mouth. Once in reach, the victim is sucked up with lightning speed. The luring apparatus is a highly evolved part of the dorsal fin and varies greatly between different species. It comprises two parts, a thin rod that is situated on the snout, and the bait at the end of the rod. Depending on the species: the length of the spine varies; and the shape at the bait unfolds into a mimic that is modelled on a small fish, invertebrate or worm. In addition, the mimic-bait is moved in the way the real thing would swim, making it very convincing indeed. Whilst some species eat almost anything that moves, others specialise in particular prey-species. Tropical species are known to produce pelagic eggs, but those living in sub-tropical zones lay eggs in reef crevices that are guarded by the female. Anglerfishes are also know as anglers (South Africa) and called frogfishes by Americans.

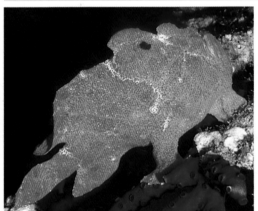 

Giant Anglerfish *Antennarius commersoni*

Adults mimic sponges, matching the colour perfectly. With large individuals, the whole fish looks like a separate sponge. Usually lives in large open caves and they are often found on jetty pylons. Large individuals mainly orange in the Maldives, but also black that are very difficult to find. Small juveniles hide in reefs and sometimes found under large rubble pieces. Widespread Indo-Pacific. Length to 35 cm.
Photo left, orange form: Jörg Aebi; right, grey form: Herwarth Voigtmann.

Clown Anglerfish *Antennarius maculatus*

Adults found in sponge areas, often silty inshore habitat. Usually yellow with saddle-like reddish patches and with wart-like swelling over body and fins. Small juveniles bright yellow or white and often found sitting on dark background, mimicking nudibranchs. Bait represents a small fish. Widespread tropical Indo-Pacific. Length to 10 cm.
Photo: Jörg Aebi.

Painted Anglerfish *Antennarius pictus*

Sheltered reefs between 3 and 50 m depth. One of the most variable species at all stages. Adults mimic sponges and corals and range from white to black, and from yellow to red. Sometimes with differently colour patches or ocelli all over. Small juveniles mimic nudibranchs and flatworms and often found on sand and rubble. Tips of pectoral fins nearly always white. Widespread tropical Indo-Pacific. Length to 16 cm.
Photo left: Camouflaged adult. Photo right: Juvenile, about 40 mm long, showings flatworm colouration. At this size it changes to couflage of sponges or other background it chooses. Photos: Jörg Aebi.

Spotfin Anglerfish *Antennarius nummifer*

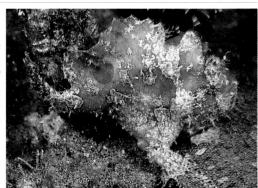

Prefers clear outer reef conditions and usually on steep walls in small crevices and in sponges. Highly variable, matching sponges of the area. A dark spot, slightly larger than eye, at base of dorsal fin is usually obvious. Has shrimp-like bait and feeds on small fishes. Widespread tropical Indo-Pacific. Length to 10 cm. Photo: Bali, Indonesia.

Freckled Anglerfish *Antennarius coccineus*

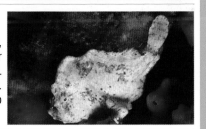

Variable from grey, brown to yellow, and sometimes reddish brown, matching habitat. Often on sponges or algae reef. Changes colour quickly when moving about and typically highly camouflaged. Reported to 75 m depth, but mostly found in less than 10 m. Widespread Indo-Pacific, ranging into subtropical waters. Length to just over 10 cm. Photo: Jörg Aebi.

Sargassum Anglerfish *Histrio histrio*

This species lives in floating sargassum weeds, especially when large amounts accumulate during the wet seasons, and drift into areas by chance. Rarely seen by divers unless purposely looking for them by going through the weeds. Produces eggs in a mucus raft amongst the weeds. Widespread Indo-Pacific.
Length to 15 cm.

Photos: Flores, Indonesia.

LIZARDFISHES - SYNODONTIDAE

A small tropical global family with 5 genera and about 50 species, of which 3 genera and at least 9 species occur in the Maldives. Genus *Harpadon*, known as Bombay Ducks, is only found in very deep water, and *Bathysaurus* the deepsea lizardfishes live in depths over 1000 m. Lizardfishes mainly hunt fishes and swimming invertebrates, taking surprisingly large prey that are swallowed whole. These efficient predators lay in ambush to strike at prey with a burst of speed. Some bury themselves in the sand with just eyes exposed. Sometimes target specific prey species, often blennies such as the sabretooth blennies, including the false cleanerfish, but most take a variety of reef fishes. The jaws have one or more series of needle-like teeth along its entire length. Some species are very similar and identification can be difficult in the wild or from photographs.

Blotched Saury *Saurida nebulosa*

Usually found partly buried in the sand, close to reef edges or on open rubble patches on reef crests. Prefers shallow coastal, often silty habitat, and enters estuaries. Usually has series of small dark blotches in line along middle of sides and two dark blotches over back. Dark blotches narrow when on light sand and broad when on dark sand. Widespread Indo-Pacific. Length to 16 cm.

Reef Saury *Saurida gracilis*

Often found resting in the open on reef rubble patches. Rather stocky compared to other species and usually with large dark blotches and strongly marked fins. Occurs in shallow coastal reefs to deep offshore, reported to 100+ m depth. Widespread Indo-Pacific. Length to 20 cm.
Photo: Bali, Indonesia.

Indian Lizardfish
Synodus indicus

The habitat in the Maldives was a sand slope whipped-up by tidal currents, quite steep, ranging from 3 to 20 m depth. The lizardfishes were common at the lower part of the slope, and seen partly buried. This species is reported throughout the Indo-Pacific, to depths of 100 m, but not often observed by divers.
Length to 33 cm, largest seen in the Maldives about 15 cm.
The photographs represent a new record for the Maldives.

Grey-streak Lizardfish *Synodus dermatogenys*

Mainly found buried in sand near reefs or in lagoons near remote bommies surrounded by sand, but also on reef. Common in the Maldives. Highly variable from sandy colour to contrasting blotching on reefs. Fins often yellowish and a bluish grey streak along upper size is usually evident. Mostly seen in less than 20 m, but reported from deep offshore as well. Widespread Indo-Pacific. Length to 22 cm.

Variegated Lizardfish *Synodus variegatus*

This species is primarily found on rubble reef and usually not buried in sand. The mid-side line comprises of more elongated blotches compared to similar species, sometimes almost forming a stripe, and usually has a reddish colour. Inshore reef crests and slopes to 25 m depth. Widespread Indo-Pacific. Length to 25 cm.

Nose-spots Lizardfish *Synodus binotatus*

Inshore to about 15 m depth. A reef species, less common and easily overlooked because of the similarity with other species. Two small black spots on the tip of the snout, usually very distinct, but these can be present in several other species. Best identified by body colour: the part in front of the dorsal fin is often lighter than the rest, as shown in photograph. Widespread Indo-Pacific. Length to 20 cm.

Tail-blotch Lizardfish *Synodus jaculum*

Shallow protected rubble-reef flats to sand flats of over 30 m depth. Sometimes swims high above the bottom, an unusual behaviour for shallow water members in this family. Easily recognised by the dark blotch on the base of the tailfin. Often has shiny green back as shown in second photograph. Pale on sand and darker on reefs. Uncommon in the Maldives, probably only deep. Widespread Indo-Pacific.
Length to 20 cm. Photo: John E. Randall.

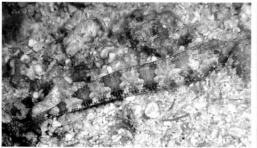

Red-marbled Lizardfish *Synodus rubromarginatus*

Usually on rubble slopes at the base of drop-offs or near remote bommies on sand in the deepest lagoons. Prefers depths of 30+ m, rarely in shallower depths. Photograph was taken in 42 m depth. Has strongly defined broad saddles that often are bright red in colour. Widespread Indo-Pacific. Length to 15 cm.

Painted Lizardfish *Trachinocephalus myops*

Found in a large depth range, from very shallow sand flats and slopes to depths of about 200 m. It typically buries itself in sand with just the eyes exposed. Usually discovered by divers when about to put a hand or knee on it, and it dashes off to quickly bury itself somewhere else. Not often seen in the Maldives and the photograph is the first record of this species for the region. Length to 25 cm. Photo, close-up: Australia.

FLASHLIGHT FISHES - ANOMALOPIDAE

A small family with 6 genera and 5 species. Only the genus *Photoblepharon* has two species, one of which occurs in the Maldives. These fishes possess a prominent light organ below the eye that is used to detect prey at night. With a black membrane the light can be blocked out to avoid predators, darting away in various directions. Light is produced by bacteria living symbiotically on a special patch of skin. During the day they live in dark caves or tunnels far into the reefs. They come out when it is dark, often rising from deep water to the shallows on moonless nights.

Red Sea Flashlight Fish
Photoblepharon steinitzi

Only seen at night along deep drop-offs where they feed on zooplankton in loose groups. Usually in depths over 25 m, but they may rise to shallower depths on dark nights in pursuit of food. Reported shallow in Red Sea area. Only known from west Indian Ocean and Red Sea area to the Maldives. A very similar species in west Pacific. Length to 11 cm.
Photo: Charles Anderson.

SQUIRRELFISHES & SOLDIERFISHES - HOLOCENTRIDAE

This large family comprises two sub-families: HOLOCENTRINAE, the squirrelfishes; and MYRIPRISTINAE, the soldierfishes. The groups are presented separately.

SQUIRRELFISHES - HOLOCENTRIDAE-1

The squirrelfishes are distinguished from soldierfishes by the much larger spine on the gill cover (venomous in some) and the more pointed head. Of the 3 genera and over thirty species, 2 genera and at least 14 species occur in the Maldives. Some species form groups in caves during the day but activities are mainly nocturnal. Many species are secretive during the day and only seen at night. During the night they hunt near the bottom for shrimps or other swimming crustaceans and small fishes. Some species are numerous in coral rich lagoons that provide good shelter during the day, but others are rarely seen because of preference for deep water along outer reef walls.

Three-spot Squirrelfish
Sargocentron melanospilos

This species was only recently found in the Maldives. An aggregation of about 20 individuals were found underneath the shipwreck 'Maldives Victoria' at 35 m depth and several more individuals photographed elsewhere in the Maldives. The colouration is slightly different from Pacific fish and matches *S. marisrubri* recently described from the Red Sea. However, scale and fin counts matches Pacific populations. Widespread Indo-Pacific.
Length to 25 cm.
Photo, aggregation above sand: shipwreck 'Maldives Victory'; individual on reef: Scott Michael.

Fine-lined Squirrelfish
Sargocentron microstoma

Occurs on shallow protected reef, singly or in small groups, often seen amongst coral during the day but rarely out in the open. Recognised by the fine red lines over each scale row and the thickened white interspace that often forms a streak below the end of the back fin. Widespread Indo-Pacific, and moderately common in the Maldives between 1 and 10 m depth. Length to 20 cm.

Crown Squirrelfish
Sargocentron diadema

The most common Maldives species in the genus, often forming aggregations near large caves and often swims openly about but stays close to the bottom. Shallow reef crests to deep along walls, to at least 30 m depth. Dorsal fin on the back has diagnostic colouration but looks almost black with natural light in deep water. Widespread Indo-Pacific. Length to 17 cm.

Blue-lined Squirrelfish
Sargocentron tiere

Occurs on semi-exposed reef flats to 20 m depth. Shy during the day, usually staying in the back of long caves. Identified by the red face markings and several reflective white lines along lower sides. In natural light the lines reflect blue. Widespread Indo-Pacific.
Length to 30 cm.
Photo: Guam.

Pink Squirrelfish
Sargocentron tiereoides

Usually only seen at night along steep slopes and walls with crevices and caves, usually common at particular sites in the Maldives, but readily dives in holes for cover when exposed. Has evenly spaced lines over the body and a distinctive pinkish look. Widespread Indo-Pacific.
Length to 16 cm.

Speckled Squirrelfish
Sargocentron punctatissimus

Mainly occurs on shallow exposed reef slopes. Occasionally seen at night along steep slopes and walls with crevices and caves on protected inner reefs. Identified by red band along top of first dorsal fin. Photo shows night colour. Paler during the day and finely dark-spotted. Widespread Indo-Pacific.
Length to 20 cm.
Photo: Sulawesi, Indonesia.

Red-face Squirrelfish
Sargocentron violaceum

A solitary and secretive species but occasionally seen during the day in the front of narrow crevices or holes in reefs. Protected clear water habitat between 5 and 30 m. Easily recognised by its distinctive colouration. Widespread Indo-Pacific.
Length to 25 cm.

White-tail Squirrelfish
Sargocentron caudimaculatum

Forms groups in caves during the day, mostly along steep slopes and walls. Shallow to about 30 m depth. Tail whitish during the day but entire fish bright red at night. Widespread Indo-Pacific.
Length to 25 cm.

Sabre Squirrelfish *Sargocentron spiniferum*

Deep lagoons to outer reefs, often with large coral heads sheltering below overhangs, to at least 30 m depth. In the Maldives often in small groups, elsewhere usually seen solitary. Also called Giant Squirrelfish, because it is the largest squirrelfish species. Widespread Indo-Pacific.
Length to 45 cm.
Photo right, red form: Toshikazu Kozawa.

Spotfin Squirrelfish
Neoniphon sammara

Usually in shallow reef crests and lagoons amongst tall corals, often in groups, to depth of about 15 m. Best recognised by the black in the dorsal fin, combined with thin lines along the body. In general, the most common species in genus. Widespread Indo-Pacific.
Length to 24 cm.

Mouthfin Squirrelfish *Neoniphon opercularis*

Usually deep along outer reef walls, secretive in crevices during the day, usually in 20+ m depth, sometimes in small groups or mixed with other squirrelfishes. Erects its white-tipped black dorsal fin when alarmed, looking like a large mouth with series of shark-like teeth. Widespread Indo-Pacific.
Largest in genus, to 35 cm long.

Silver Squirrelfish
Neoniphon argenteus

Mostly a lagoon species, in the Maldives common in large isolated coral heads in less than 10 m depth. Usually in small groups, scattered through the corals. Recognised by the lack of lines or black in dorsal fin. Widespread Indo-Pacific. Length to 25 cm.

Yellow-striped Squirrelfish
Neoniphon aurolineatus

A rarely observed species that prefers depths of 40+ m throughout its Indo-Pacific range. In the Maldives in outer reef waters. Has distinctive thin yellow lines along its body.
Length to 22 cm.
Photo: Mustag Hussain.

SOLDIERFISHES - HOLOCENTRIDAE-2

Large group with about 70 species worldwide, 8 of which known from the Maldives. Soldierfishes have extremely large eyes and a blunt snout. They are nocturnal, feeding mainly in open water away from reef or walls on large zooplankton such as shrimp and crab larvae, but during the day some species congregate in large open caves or below overhangs of reef. Some species swim against the ceilings inverted, their belly towards it or to the sides, whilst in the same group other individuals may swim the normal way. Some species and most juveniles are extremely secretive and are only seen at night, swimming above corals or near the bottom. Most species are found in depths less than 30 m, but some venture deeper. Some species were also known as squirrelfishes, but this name is now reserved for the previous group. Photo above: *Myripristis vittata* schooling in cave.

Immaculate Soldierfish *Myripristis vittata*

White-tipped Soldierfish. Forms schools in caves, mostly along walls to at least 30 m depth. Often swims inverted on ceilings. First dorsal fin has distinct white tips at the end of each spine. Widespread Indo-Pacific. Probably the most common soldierfish throughout its range, including in the Maldives
Length to 20 cm.

Big-eyed Soldierfish
Myripristis pralinia

Shallow protected inner reefs, usually shallow to 15 m depth. Secretive during the day, usually only seen at night swimming above corals but quickly dives for cover when exposed to get away from the light. Widespread Indo-Pacific.
Length to 20 cm.

Crimson Soldierfish
Myripristis murdjan

Often seen solitary on shallow coastal reefs but enters deep water and commonly found inside shipwrecks. Several very similar species with white edges on fins. This species has large scales and red first dorsal fin. Probably not as common as suggested in literature as name often applied to other species. Widespread Indo-Pacific.
Length to 25 cm.

Yellow-fin Soldierfish *Myripristis berndti*

Mostly found in clear water lagoons and protected reefs, sheltering below reef overhangs in small groups during the day to depths of about 25 m. Almost identical to Crimson Soldierfish, but has yellow first dorsal fin. Widespread Indo-Pacific.
Length to 30 cm.

Epaulette Soldierfish
Myripristis kuntee

Usually forms groups that swim in front of large caves. A pale looking soldierfish that is common on shallow reef slopes as well as ranging to moderate depths along outer reef walls. Widespread Indo-Pacific.
Length to 20 cm.

Violet Soldierfish
Myripristis violacea

In clear water protected reef habitat from deep lagoons to outer reefs, usually in depths over 20 m. A moderately common species in the Maldives that may be pink or pale with dark outlines of each scale, depending on its mood. Widespread Indo-Pacific.
Length to 25 cm.

Splendid Soldierfish
Myripristis botche

Usually in depths of 20+ m, with large shelving coral heads, and swimming openly around them. In natural light they look almost white with black fins, as colour red is filtered-out by the blue water. Uncommon in the Maldives, but occurs in groups where found. Until recently known as *M. melanosticta*. Widespread Indo-Pacific.
Length to 25 cm.
Photo top, pair:
Flores, Indonesia.
Photo below, in natural light.

Shadowfin Soldierfish
Myripristis adusta

Occurs singly or in pairs near large reef overhangs, in the Maldives usually in depths from 10 to at least 40 m depth. Has dark spot rather than bar behind head compared to similar species. Largest species that is often noticed by divers. Widespread Indo-Pacific.
Length to 35 cm.

SEAMOTHS - PEGASIDAE

Small Indo-Pacific family with 2 genera and 5 species, one of which reported from the Maldives. Peculiar little fishes with a bony body and produced snout, latter with protractible mouth underneath. Body plates are like in pipefishes, but body is highly depressed. The paired ventral fins below the body are reduced to slender but strong structures that, in combination with the large side fins, are used to walk with. The large pectoral fins gave them the common name of seamoth. Diet comprises tiny bottom creatures.

Little Dragonfish *Eurypegasus draconis*

An easily overlooked species that usually matches the sandy colour on which it lives. Juveniles often mimic bits of shell of the area. Adults usually bury themselves during the day and divers usually discover them by accident. Only during the spawning period are they easily seen, when the female is gravid and at dusk males are courting with colours changed for the occasion. Sheltered bays to depths of about 15 m.
Length to 8 cm. The Slender Seamoth *Pegasis volitans* is likely to be found in the Maldives as it has a long pelagic stage.
Photo, adults: Bali, Indonesia; juvenile Jörg Aebi.

TRUMPETFISHES - AULOSTOMIDAE

Family with a single genus and two species divided between Pacific and Atlantic. A cunning predator, feeding primarily on small fishes.

Trumpetfish *Aulostomus chinensis*

Coastal to outer reefs, often along upper edge of slopes. Variable brown, grey with various markings, juvenile often banded or lined, and a bright yellow form occurs commonly in the Maldives. Matches colour and swims very close to larger bottom feeding fishes to get close to unsuspecting prey. Often rests in deep water along walls in large black corals. Widespread Indo-Pacific. Length reported to 90 cm, rarely exceeds 60 cm.

FLUTEMOUTHS - FISTULARIIDAE

A single genus family with 4 species worldwide, one of which commonly seen in shallow depths on tropical reefs of the Indo-Pacific. Inhabits shallow coastal reefs as well as deep water. Sometimes seen in small schools swimming near the bottom on reef crests. At night usually near the bottom over sand flats. Diet comprises primarily other fishes.

Smooth Flutemouth
Fistularia commersonii

Usually found in protected areas, swimming near the bottom above sand or rubble areas near reef during the day in various habitats from silty lagoons to outer reefs. Reported to depths in excess of 100 m. Large individuals are usually deep and may come to the shallow at night to feed. Widespread Indo-Pacific.
Length to 1.5 m.

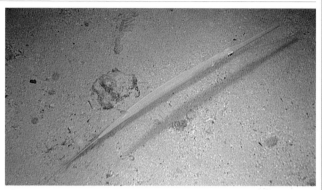

GHOSTPIPEFISHES - SOLENOSTOMIDAE

Small tropical Indo-Pacific family, comprising a single genus and at least 5 species, 3 of which known from the Maldives. Closely related and superficially very similar to the true pipefishes, but have large fins, and in addition it's the female that incubates the eggs in a pouch, instead of the male. Preliminary studies suggest that males may become females. Pelagic larvae reach a large size before settling on the bottom. Post-larvae are about half adult size and almost transparent, colouring up and growing quickly after settling. Most species swim near vertically with the head down, searching near the bottom for small invertebrates. Often along reef margins near feather stars or weeds, depending on the species. Occurrence in the Maldives probably intermittent as these fishes appear to live annually and could be expatriates from continental waters.

Ornate Ghostpipefish *Solenostomus paradoxus*
Occasionally seen in the Maldives, usually close to gorgonian or soft corals. Colour highly variable from pale with pinkish spots to near black with some red markings. Identified by the normally elaborate colour patterns or the regularly placed many narrow skin flaps on the snout. A common species elsewhere in the Indo-Pacific, found from few to about 25 m depth. Sometimes in pairs or small groups.
Length to 10 cm.
Photos left and centre, both females: Jörg Aebi; close-up right of eggs: Flores, Indonesia.

Coralline Ghostpipefish
Solenostomus sp 1

Mimics coralline algae *Halimeda macroloba*, and is easily overlooked. The algae grows on sandy and rubbly substrate and in the Maldives often on the bottom of caves along slopes and drop-offs. This undescribed species that is also known from Malaysia and Indonesia and appears to be widespread Indo-Pacific. Found to depths of 15 m. Small species, adult about 65 mm, which is smaller than the postlarval stage of other similar species it was confused with before. Photo: Jörg Aebi.

Robust Ghostpipefish *Solenostomus cyanopterus*

Mimics seagrass and varies in colour from green to dark brown. Normally found on the edge of seagrass beds, floating with separate small patches of seagrass, and commonly forms pairs. Also on reef with rich algae growth to 15 m depth. Widespread Indo-Pacific. Largest species, grows to 15 cm in some areas, commonly 12 cm. Photos: Jörg Aebi.

PIPEFISHES - SYNGNATHIDAE

Large family with over 50 genera and about 220 species worldwide, of which 8 genera and 14 species have been recorded from the Maldives. More can be expected. This highly diverse family is unique in its reproductive methods, in which the female takes the eggs to the sperm. She deposits them into a pouch or onto the underside of the body of the male, where they become embedded into the skin and are fertilised during that process. The male becomes pregnant and incubates the eggs for almost one month, giving birth to young that are either pelagic or ready to settle on the bottom. Much of the reproductive activities are related to big tides that phase with the moon cycle. Diet comprises small crawling or swimming invertebrates such as mysids and larval shrimps.

Photo below, a common shallow water species: *Corythoichthys haematopterus.*

Reef-top Pipefish
Corythoichtys haematopterus

A common shallow water species on rubble and sand patches or along reef edges, usually in depths of a few metres. Often found in pairs and males are sometimes obvious by their swollen pouch, about halfway along their body. Males have a series of dark blotched along the pouch. Widespread Indo-Pacific.
Length to 17 cm.

Schultz's Pipefish
Corythoichtys schultzi

Occurs in various habitats from protected shallow sand-rubble flats to rubble patches on reefs and in deeper lagoons to about 20 m depth. Often in areas with sparse algae or soft coral growth. Snout long and usually with several small white spots. Body has a longitudinal lined pattern. Widespread Indo-Pacific.
Length to 16 cm.

Yellow-banded Pipefish
Corythoichtys flavofasciatus

Commonly occurs on coarse rubble with dead coral pieces or in harbours where pieces or piled. Usually found in pairs in depths of a few metres. Snout short compared to other similar species. Body with diffused dark banded pattern, with yellow scribbled lines in between. Widespread Indo-Pacific, but some variations.
Length to 15 cm.

Cheeked Pipefish
Corythoichtys insularis

Moderately common in the Maldives, found along outer reef walls on rubble on the bottom of caves or ledges, usually occurs in pairs. Mainly known from depths between 15 and 40 m. Snout long and head with large dark spots. Body with evenly spaced pale, thin vertical bands. Western Indian Ocean only.
Length to 12 cm.

Long-snout Stick Pipefish *Trachyrhamphus bicoarctatus*

Easily overlooked, looking just like a stick laying on the sand, and coloured like similar items on the bottom nearby. Black to brown or yellow with series of evenly spaced light bands, or finely spotted. Head at slight angle to the body and it raises the front part of the body above the sand. The Long-snout Stick Pipefish prefers current channels, but is also found in still lagoons or in slight current zones with mixed algae, sand or rubble or habitat. Widespread Indo-Pacific, and reaches a length to about 40 cm.

Short-bodied Pipefish
Choeroichthys brachysoma

A secretive species, usually found in sheltered seagrass beds under dead coral pieces or with dark objects. Identified by shape and colour. Deep-bodied and dark brown with few white spots. Shallow to about 20 m depth. Widespread Indo-Pacific.
Length to 65 mm.
Photo: Mabul, Malaysia.

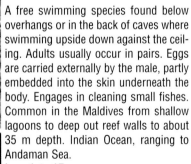

Many-bands Pipefish
Dunckerocampus multiannulatus

A free swimming species found below overhangs or in the back of caves where swimming upside down against the ceiling. Adults usually occur in pairs. Eggs are carried externally by the male, partly embedded into the skin underneath the body. Engages in cleaning small fishes. Common in the Maldives from shallow lagoons to deep out reef walls to about 35 m depth. Indian Ocean, ranging to Andaman Sea.
Length to 17 cm.

Blue-stripe Pipefish
Doryrhamphus exicus

Secretive in coral-heads in shallow lagoons, including in seagrass beds. Adults usually in pairs and usually seen swimming upside-down against the ceilings of caves or overhangs. Yellow to bright orange and a bright blue mid-lateral stripe. Widespread tropical Indo-Pacific.
Length to 65 mm. Photo: Indonesia.

Double-chin Pipefish
Doryrhamphus bicarinatus

A secretive but common species in the back of caves or narrow passages of lagoon coral bommies, often in cleaning stations with shrimps and participate in picking parasitic crustaceans from other fishes for food. Adults in pairs and often together with the Many-bands Pipefish. Males of this species have two bony knobs under the snout. First record for the Maldives, previously only known from east African coast.
Length to 80 mm.

Common Seahorse
Hippocampus kuda

Seahorses are rare in the Maldives and appear to be expatriates from mainland waters. This species often attaches itself to floating weeds and could be expected to come in to Maldives waters during the wet season. It is recognised by the smooth body and low crown on head.
Length to 20 cm.
Photo right: aquarium by Charles Anderson; left, adult: Indonesia.

Spiny Seahorse
Hippocampus hystrix

The spiny seahore prefers deeper water and usually found amongst sparse seagrass beds. Adults often singly. Easily recognised by spiny back. Like the common seahorse, it occurs widespread Indo-Pacific, and can be expected in the Maldives.
Length to 15 cm.
Photos: Indonesia.

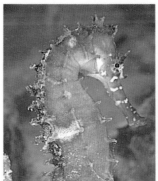
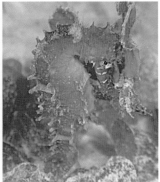

FLYING GURNARDS - DACTYLOPTERIDAE

Small family with 2 genera and 7 species worldwide, and one reported from the Maldives. They feature very large wing-like fins that are used for display. In small juveniles it often possesses a large eye-like mark that is suddenly displayed when approached. In addition part of the fin have thickened free rays near the head that are used for walking and probing the bottom to disturb prey. The fins that throw a large shade may also assist to catch prey.

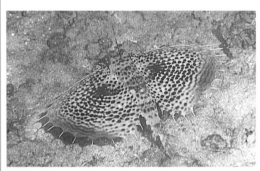

Flying Gurnard *Dactylopus orientalis*

Very rare in the Maldives and possible expatriates from pelagic larval stages that drifted into the area from continental waters. Enters shallow sandy bays adjacent to deep water. Spreads out the large fins when approached but may suddenly put them alongside and swims out of sight with a burst of speed. Feeds on bottom fishes. Widespread Indo-Pacific.
Length to 30 cm.
Photo right : Jörg Aebi; left, Java, Indonesia.

LIONFISHES & SCORPIONFISHES - SCORPAENIDAE

A large and complicated family, dividable in at least 10 sub-families, with an estimated 70 genera and 350 species globally. Several groups are not well known. About 25 species have been recorded from the Maldives but more can be expected. This family includes many venomous and potentially dangerous species, such as stonefish and lionfish, but all scorpionfishes are capable of giving nasty stings with their dorsal fin spines. The fin is raised when the fish is alarmed and it may charge if cornered. Stings are usually caused when handling the fish, or when accidentally touched. The venom is neutralised by heat. Apart from lionfishes, most species have excellent camouflage and hide in reefs. Some are rarely seen, living very deep or secretively inside reefs, and only known from specimens trawled or collected with chemicals. Diet comprises fishes and mobile invertebrates. Only those likely to be seen by divers are included here. Below: adult Common Lionfish.

Common Lionfish
Pterois volitans

The best known lionfish, easily recognised by the long feathery fins. Some variation between continental and oceanic populations. Continental form, often referred to as *P. miles*, not in the Maldives. Lives in various habitats from remote coral bommies in lagoons to caves along deep drop-offs. Hunt small fishes and uses the large fins to corner it. Widespread Indo-Pacific. Length 35 cm.
Photo right: juvenile.

Spotfin Lionfish *Pterois antennata*

Commonly occurs on coral reefs, usually at coral bases in well protected surroundings or in holes with tail towards front. Most common where some algae growth, in depths between 6 and 30 m. Widespread Indo-Pacific.
Length to 20 cm.

White-lined Lionfish *Pterois radiata*

Prefers habitat with no or little hard coral growth. Mainly in dead coral areas with algae or other non-stinging type of growth, including caves along steep slopes, to about 25 m depth. Identified by dark general colour and thin white lines. Widespread Indo-Pacific, but rare in many areas.
Length to 20 cm.

Zebra Lionfish *Dendrochirus zebra*

In the Maldives mainly found in silty still lagoons and harbours, often with remote debris or rubble piles on sand. Shallow to deep sand flats with large coral heads, probably in excess of 45 m. Reported to 80 m in some areas elsewhere. Widespread Indo-Pacific. Length to 20 cm.
Photo, left: Jörg Aebi.

Dwarf Lionfish
Dendrochirus brachypterus

Various habitats with sponges and algae, usually common under jetties on pylon crossings or on deep remote reef outcrops on sand. Variable in colour from brown to red with light or dark bands, rarely bright yellow. Widespread Indo-Pacific.
Length to 15 cm.

Two-eyed Lionfish *Dendrochirus biocellatus*

The least observed lionfish. Mainly nocturnal, living in sponges and caves in sheltered reefs. Comes out at night and seen openly on shallow reef flats where they hunt for shrimps. Rare in the Maldives. Widespread Indo-Pacific, but generally not common.
Length to 13 cm.
Photos: Bali, Indonesia.

Common Scorpionfish
Scorpaenodes guamensis

A small secretive species, usually found when turning over dead coral pieces in shallow lagoons or well protected reef flats. Several very similar species, best recognised by a large dark blotch on the gills. Widespread and locally common in varies areas of the Indo-Pacific.
Length to 12 cm.
Photo: Bali, Indonesia.

Shortfin Scorpionfish
Scorpaenodes parvipinnis

A small species that is usually seen on night dives along inshore reef walls with dominant algae growth or on sponges. Recognised by the large pale body area behind the head. Depth range 10 to 50 m. Widespread Indo-Pacific.
Length to 85 mm.
Photo: Bali, Indonesia.

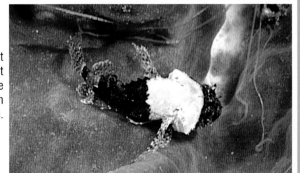

Blotchfin Scorpionfish
Scorpaenodes varipinnis

A well camouflaged species in coastal reefs to 20 m depth, sometimes on jetty pylons with good sponge growth. A dark looking fish with red markings on the head and fin bases. Widespread Indo-Pacific.
Length to 12 cm.
Photo: Sulawesi, Indonesia.

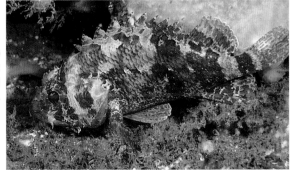

False Stonefish *Scorpaenopsis diabola*

Distinctive species by the large and unusually shaped head that looks like a piece of dead coral. Well camouflaged among coral rubble in shallow protected reef flats and harbours. Often mistaken for a stonefish. Widespread Indo-Pacific. Length to 18 cm.
Photo left, adult: Neville Coleman; right, juvenile: Toshikazu Kozawa.

Smallscale Scorpionfish *Scorpaenopsis oxycephala*

The largest scorpionfish in the Maldives where it is common on sheltered reefs from a few metres depth to about 20 m. Often seen at night when it is more out in the open, possibly because the artificial light shows the fish colour better. Widespread Indo-Pacific. Length to 35 cm.
Phot0 left: Toshikazu Kozawa; right: Neville Coleman.

Coral Scorpionfish
Sebastapistes cyanostigma

A small colourful species that lives between branches of fire corals or in protection of other stinging corals. Usually shallow surge zones along the top of drop-offs with rich coral growth. Pink with yellow spots all over. At night spots are white. Widespread Indo-Pacific. Length to 10 cm.
Photo: Bali, Indonesia.

Barchin Scorpionfish
Sebastapistes strongia

A well camouflaged small species, found under coral rubble or amongst the bases of coral branches. Sheltered coastal reefs and harbours, often in depths of a few metres. Mottled colour pattern and often large tentacles above eyes. Widespread Indo-Pacific. Length to 6 cm.

Reef Stonefish *Synanceia verrucosa*

Mainly occurs in still places on reef crest with mixed coral and algae cover and in harbours amongst large coral rubble pieces, often partly buried. Most dangerous stinger. Venom injected by the spines on the back causes excruciating pain and can kill, several deaths reported. Widespread Indo-Pacific. Length to 38 cm.
Photo left: Harbour colour (Malé harbour). Photo right, reef colour: Jörg Aebi.

Paper Scorpionfish
Taenianotus triacanthus

Recognised by the flat body with sailfin-like fin over the back, but easily overlooked. Highly variable to suit surroundings from white, dark purplish brown to bright yellow and pink. Often next to sponges or on top of corals. Clear coastal to outer reef habitat from shallow depths to reported depth of 135 m. Widespread Indo-Pacific.
Length to 10 cm.
Photos, showing colour variations: Jörg Aebi.

WASPFISHES - TETRAROGIDAE

A moderate sized family of small and often little known species with an estimated 15 genera and 40 species. Only two species are known from the Maldives. Similar to scorpionfishes but fin over the top well forward on head, starting in front of the eyes. Most species live on soft bottom, mixed rubble, algae or weeds and sponges. Diet comprises mainly small invertebrates.

Spiny Leaf-Fish *Ablabys macracanthus*

Protected still habitats, adults on moderately deep soft-bottom slopes to about 50 m depth, juveniles sometimes shallow in sparse seagrass beds. Variable in colour from grey and yellowish brown to dark brown to almost black. Known from scattered Indo-Pacific localities, including Indonesia, Malaysia and Philippines. Length to 18 cm. Photo left, adults: Flores, Indonesia; right, juvenile: Mabul, Malaysia

Indian Leaf-Fish
Ablabys binotatus

Soft-bottom habitats with sponge, coralline-algae growth and weeds. Well camouflaged and mainly active on dusk, sometimes moving onto more open areas. Subtidal to 25 m depth. Very similar to the Spiny Leaf-fish, but has a taller dorsal fin that is pointed high above the head, and has less rays in the anal fin. West Indian Ocean only.
Length to 15 cm.
Photo: Herwarth Voigtmann.

FLATHEADS - PLATYCEPHALIDAE

Large family, primarily Indo-Pacific, with estimated 18 genera and 60 species. Most are restricted in mainland waters and only a few are encountered by divers in the Maldives. Included here are two common species. Most tropical species are small, reaching about 30 cm, and especially during the day are buried in the sand with just eyes exposed. At night they are more active and occasionally sit on top of the sand. They feed on fishes and swimming invertebrates such as squid. They have large flattened, bony heads that are often armed with spiny ridges.

Fringe-lip Flathead
Thysanophrys otaitensis

Shallow sand- and mud-flats, only out at night. Usually in small spread-out groups in sheltered bays. Several similar species, This species has strongly marked ventral and pectoral fins from spotted to almost all black. Widespread Indo-Pacific.
Length to 25 cm.
Photo: Indonesia.

Long-snout Flathead
Thysanophrys chiltonae

Coarse sand and mud-slopes, usually between 6 and 25 m depth. Mainly out at night. Best identified by double dusky bar below eye and white-marked ventral and pectoral fins. Widespread Indo-Pacific.
Length to 25 cm.
Photo: Indonesia.

SOAPFISHES, ROCK CODS, GROUPERS & BASSLETS - SERRANIDAE

Large and complicated family of many distinctly different groups, and future studies will probably separate these into families in their own right. Including all the various groups there are about 50 genera and well over 400 species. For simplifications the various groups are presented here separately as part of the family Serranidae.

SOAPFISHES - SERRANIDAE-1

A small group of fishes that have a toxin in the skin that is released under stress to deter predators. The toxin can kill other fishes if collected and kept together in small containers, and can cause irritations to human skin in sensitive areas. The Yellow Soapfish has bright colours and swims openly about, its juveniles often mimic venomous blennies as well and are left alone by predators. Other species are more shy and stay under reef cover or very close to crevices. Prey consists primarily of fishes and shrimps. Included with this group are the reef basslets that are closely related. These are small active hunters that live in the back of large caves.

Snowflake Soapfish *Pogonoperca ocellata*

Occurs on sparse reef or found around small coral bommies along the bases of reefs. A rare fish in general, appears to prefer moderate depth in the Maldives from about 30 m down. Photograph taken at Maalhoss in 42 m, representing first record for the Maldives. West Indian Ocean only, replaced by sibling *P. punctata* in the Pacific and Christmas Islands in the east Indian Ocean. Length to 33 cm.
Photo, close-up: Toshikazu Kozawa.

Lined Soapfish
Grammistes sexlineatus

Juveniles commonly found in shallow protected reef flats and slopes among large coral rubble pieces until about 15 cm long. Adults appear to move to very deep water and are rarely seen. Reported to over 150 m depth and the large adults have series of elongated spots were the lines of their earlier stages were. Widespread Indo-Pacific.
Length to 27 cm.
Photo, tiny juvenile: Toshikazu Kozawa.

Yellow Soapfish
Diploprion bifasciatum

Also known as Yellow Emperor. Prefers silty reefs and harbour conditions, patchy occurrence in the Maldives. Widespread Indo-Pacific, usually common in continental waters. Adults often in small groups below jetties with large rock or boulder formations. Has large mouth and feeds primarily on other fishes.
Length to 25 cm.
Photo: John E. Randall.

Arrow-headed Soapfish
Belonoperca chabanaudi

Typically lives in small dark caves, staying in the shade when at the entrance. Usually the yellow blotch is noticed whilst the rest is absorbed in the background. Mainly occurs along outer reef walls in about 20 m depth. Widespread Indo-Pacific where found in various depths. Length to 15 cm.

African Reef Basslet
Liopropoma africanum

Common in the Maldives but lives in the network of tunnels and crevices that are typically in the back of large overhanging reefs or caves along the outer reef slopes and wall. They are usually discovered when using a torch and quickly disappear, but show some curiosity and turning off the light may bring them back. West Indian Ocean only, occurring in depths to 50 m. Length to 85 mm.

Pinstriped Reef Basslet
Liopropoma susumi

Lives in the back of large caves along outer reef walls, secretively moving through narrow crevices or tunnels, usually seen solitary. Moderately common in the Maldives in depths to at least 30 m, sometimes in shallow lagoons. Identified by thin longitudinal lines. Widespread Indo-Pacific.
Length to 92 mm.

The largest group includes the groupers, sometimes called cods or rock cods, usually in relation to a particular genus. Most species reach a moderate size for a reef fish and the largest, the Giant or Queensland Grouper (sometimes spelt groper) is reported to 3 m length. The smallest are about 20 cm long but most grow well over 30 cm in length. Nearly all of the Maldives species live on reefs where adults often swim openly about, but when approached they are quick to dive for cover if not used to divers. A few species can be found on open sand substrate but these are usually in close vicinity of some solid objects with places to hide. Juveniles are secretive and stay in the protection of reefs. Diet comprises a variety of mobile invertebrates and fishes, and some species are cunning predators. Latter, when juvenile, mimic small mouthed wrasses to get close to unsuspected prey. Most adult groupers are active on dusk, taking advantage of the confusion or arguments between other fishes when many are looking for sleeping places in reefs, the best time for potential prey. Habitats range from shallow lagoons to deep outer reefs, depending on the species.

Indian Coral Grouper *Plectropomus pessuliferus*

Generally a rare species known mainly from Indian Ocean, but also known from localities such as Fiji in the Pacific. It is occasionally sighted along outer reef slopes in the Maldives and recorded from depths between 20 and 145 m. Population in the Red Sea is differently coloured and regarded as a sub-species.
Length to 60 cm, reported to 90 cm.

Squaretail Coral Grouper
Plectropomus areolatus

A common Maldives fish, often numerous in large and deep lagoons but a rather flighty fish in general. In depths from shallow reef channels to about 30 m depth, occasionally on deeper slopes. Recognised by the straight vertical edge of the caudal fin. Widespread Indo-Pacific. Length to 75 cm, rarely over 60 cm.

Black-saddle Coral Grouper
Plectropomus laevis

A moderately common fish throughout the Indo-Pacific. Juveniles and semi-adults in their bright 'footballer' colours are readily recognised. Small juveniles mimic the Saddled Pufferfish that is poisonous. Juveniles in various depths, and adults venture well beyond diving depths, occurring inshore to outer reef habitats.
Length to at least 1 m.

Vermilion Rock Cod *Cephalopholis miniata*

Also called Coral Rock cod. One of the most common shallow water reef species throughout the Indo-Pacific, including the Maldives. Small juveniles are without spots and more like basslets but stay close to the corals. Adults sometimes in small groups, usually to depths of about 20 m, sometimes deeper. Length to 40 cm.

Six-spot Rock Cod
Cephalopholis sexmaculata

Widespread and common Indo-Pacific species, including the Maldives, but usually found in large caves and below overhangs of reef along deep walls from 6 to at least 50 m depth. Often swims vertically or upside down, orientating the belly to the nearest part of the reef. Length to 45 cm.

Peacock Rock Cod
Cephalopholis argus

Found in various coral habitats, in the Maldives mainly on reef crests in 6 to 10 m but ventures into deep water at times. Often seen resting in the shade of overhanging corals. Identified by colouration, often white blotch in front of pectoral fin base. Widespread Indo-Pacific. length to 45 cm.

Dusky-banded Rock Cod
Cephalopholis boenak

Prefers silty coastal and protected inner reefs and is uncommon in the Maldives. Common in continental waters where it lives in shallow reefs to about 20 m depth. Identified by the dusky broad bands over the body. Widespread Indo-Pacific.
Length to 30 cm.
Photo: Java, Indonesia.

Tomato Rock Cod *Cephalopholis sonnerati*

A common widespread Indo-Pacific continental species, ranging to over 100 m. In the Maldives it appears to be restricted to deep water and found on isolated coral bommies on sand slopes in 30+ m depth. Changes drastic in colour from juvenile to adult, and adults may display a blotched pattern at times. Length to 50 cm.

Orange Rock Cod
Cephalopholis spiloparaea

Mainly found on reef slopes and walls in depths over 20 m, especially inner reef slopes that are slightly silty. Moderately common in the Maldives and best identified from the next species, the Blackfin Rock Cod, by the pale pectoral fins on the sides and usually some white at the corners of the caudal fin.
Length to 25 cm.

Blackfin Rock Cod *Cephalopholis nigripinnis*

Easily confused with Orange Rock Cod above but lacks white in the tail and has dusky pectoral fins when adult. Moderately common in the Maldives on reef crests with rich coral growth. Widespread Indian Ocean, east to Java, replaced by Flagtail Rockcod *C. urodeta* in the Pacific, that is readily recognised by white stripes in the tail. Length to 30 cm.

Leopard Rock Cod
Cephalopholis leoparda

Smallest in genus, best recognised by tail pattern. Variable from light brown to bright orange or red, but tail-pattern always diagnostic. Common on rich coral reefs from inshore to outer reef, in 3 to 25 m depth. Widespread Indo-Pacific.
Length to 20 cm.

Harlequin Rock Cod *Cephalopholis polleni*

Usually found deep along outer reef drop-offs from 10 to 50+ metres, usually staying in the shade of large caves and overhangs. Easily recognised by ornamental colours. Juveniles pinkish with yellow. A rare species in the Maldives. Appears to be widespread Indo-Pacific, common in Indonesia. Length to 35 cm.
Photo: Jörg Aebi.

White-square Grouper *Gracila albomarginata*

Uncommon in the Maldives but can be seen along deep water drop-offs, sometimes swimming into shallow reef crest areas in less than 6 m, but ranges to at least 70 m. May follow divers when they are not aware but quickly move off when approached. Widespread Indo-Pacific. Length to 45 cm. Photo, juvenile: Kerama, Japan.

Red-flushed Grouper *Aethaloperca rogaa*

Juveniles often in rich coral growth on shallow reef crests. Adults on reef slopes with large caves and often in shipwrecks to at least 50 m depth, and recognised as a species by the plain dark grey colour and deep body. Widespread Indo-Pacific. Length to 70 cm.

Lunar-tailed Grouper *Variola louti*

Common on outer reef slopes and walls in the Maldives, often in surge zones. Small juveniles are secretive in reefs but individuals between about 15 and 25 cm were openly swimming about and swimming with *Paruneneus macronema*, the Long-barble Goatfish, and obviously a case of mimicry in the Maldives, matching their colour perfectly. Widespread Indo-Pacific.
Length to 80 cm, but usually large adults move to deep water. Photo, juvenile: Scott Michael.

White-edged Lyretail *Variola albimarginata*

Mainly seen along deep outer reef walls in the Maldives in depth of 30+ m. It is distinguished from the previous species by a white edge, rather then yellow on the end of the tail fin and general colouration of the adult and juvenile. Widespread Indo-Pacific. Length to 65 cm.

Foursaddle Grouper *Epinephelus spilotoceps*

Common in the Maldives on shallow reef crests and slopes with good coral growth to about 20 m depth. Appears to come out mainly on dusk. Spotting small on head, and black saddles usually distinctive in adults but occasionally are absent. Widespread Indo-Pacific. Length to 35 cm.

Black-spot Grouper
Epinephelus melanostigma

Rarely seen in the Maldives, preferring inshore and often silty reef habitats with mixed algae and coral growth. Usually in depth less than 10 m. Idenfied by black saddle spot on back. Widespread Indo-Pacific. Length to 35 cm.
Photo: Sunda Strait, Indonesia.

Greasy Grouper
Epinephelus tauvina

Clear water lagoons in outer reef zones from shallow reef flats to about 50 m depth. Distinguished from similar species by the similar sized spots on body and snout, usually smaller on snout in the other species. Widespread Indo-Pacific.
Length to 70 cm. Photo: Scott Michael.

Snubnose Grouper *Epinephelus macrospilos*

Mainly seen on outer reef slopes in the Maldives, and fairly common in surge zones between 6 and 10 m depth. A rather shy species in rich coral growth areas. Widespread Indo-Pacific, Indian Ocean populations have larger spots compared to Pacific ones. Length to 50 cm. Photo right, adult with cleaner-wrasse: Java, Indonesia.

Honeycomb Grouper *Epinephelus merra*

The most common and one of the smaller species, often abundant in some shallow reefs, from coastal silty habitat to outer reefs. In deep lagoons to about 25 m depth. In adults the dark blotches centrally along sides often join, forming short horizontal bands in the darker areas. Widepread Indo-Pacific.
Length to 28 cm.

Small-spotted Grouper *Epinephelus caeruleopunctatus*

Mainly found on inner reefs and sheltered lagoons. Juveniles often in brackish water during the wet season. Shallow habitat, usually in less than 20 m in the Maldives. Variously spotted with small dark spots and often mixed with larger white rounded blotched of mixed sized, some eye-sized. Widespread Indo-Pacific.
Length to 60 cm. Photo right, adult: Toshikazu Kozawa; left, juvenile Flores, Indonesia.

White-speckled Grouper *Epinephelus ongus*

Usually seen solitary in caves with rich invertebrate growth along outer reef walls and slopes from 10 m down. Juveniles secretively in corals. Widespread Indo-Pacific, but uncommon in the Maldives. Body dark with pale spots that extend over the fins, sometimes with large pale blotches over the body. Length to 35 cm.
Photo right, adult: Charles Anderson; left, juvenile: Flores, Indonesia.

 69

Squaretail Grouper
Epinephelus areolatus

Not commonly seen in the Maldives. Prefers silty bottom, often open sand with small coral heads or solid debris with coverage. Usually in depths over 10 m, often deep along the base of slopes where the bottom becomes flat. Recognised by the straight edge ending the tail with a thin white edge. Widespread Indo-Pacific.
Length to 40 cm.
Photograph in Bali, Indonesia.

Long-spined Grouper *Epinephelus longispinis*

Prefers silty reef conditions, often in sheltered muddy places with remote coral pieces or debris on open bottom. Juveniles with weeds on rocks or dead coral pieces in depths between inter-tidal to over 30 m. This species is widespread Indian Ocean, ranging into the west Pacific to Flores, Indonesia. Length to 55 c m

Snout-spots Grouper *Epinephelus polyphekadion*

Moderately common throughout the Maldives, usually in crevices and small caves of protected reefs to about 20 m depth. Best identified by double black spots on tip of snout, but maybe obscured in large individuals that can look very similar to the flower cod (next species). Widespread Indo-Pacific.
Length to 75 cm.
Photo left, juvenile: Flores, Indonesia; above, intermediate: Japan, Aquarium.

Wavy-lined Grouper
Epinephelus undulosus

Typically found on open silty-sand and muddy habitat. Usually a flighty species that dives into holes of remote bommies or under pieces of debris. Widespread Indo-Pacific, mainly mainland waters and rare in the Maldives.
Length to 45 cm.
Photo: Flores, Indonesia.

Flower Grouper *Epinephelus fuscoguttatus*

The most common large species in many areas of the Maldives, adults usually in or near large caves from deep lagoons to outer reef slopes, but mostly in shallow depths to about 10 m. Juveniles in other areas are known to enter brackish, near freshwater habitats. Widespread Indo-Pacific.
Length to 90 cm. Photo, juvenile: Flores, Indonesia.

Giant Grouper *Epinephelus lanceolatus*

The largest in the genus. Not uncommon in the Maldives but usually seen as adult along deep outer reef slopes or on current-prone channel reefs, often well over 1 m long. Juveniles as secretive and everywhere rarely seen until changing to adult colours. Widespread Indo-Pacific, called Queensland Groper in Australia. Length to 2 m, reported much larger in some areas. Photo, adult: Helmut Debelius; close-up: Singapore Aquarium.

Blacktip Grouper *Epinephelus fasciatus*

Common in the Maldives on clear water reef crests, in 6 m depth, but ranges to deep water as well. Some geographical variations, and in the Maldives variable between depths, some forms shows no banding at all. Widespread Indo-Pacific. Sometimes called Red-barred Cod. Length to 35 cm.
Photo left, banded form: Neville Coleman.

Yellow-fin Grouper *Epinephelus flavocaeruleus*

A common mainland species that occurs in shallow protected reefs and lagoons in the Maldives but in a few places, often under jetties at resorts. Widespread Indian Ocean, ranging to Bali, Indonesia, replaced by sibling *E. cyanopodus* in the Pacific that differs primarily in lacking yellow fins when adult.
Length to 90 cm, based on records. Photo left, adult: Jörg Aebi.

White-lined Grouper *Anyperodon leucogrammicus*

Shallow reef crests to moderately deep slopes with tall coral coverage but rarely deeper than 25 m. Adults may occur in small loose groups that swim in the protection of the corals. Small juveniles mimic small mouthed striped wrasses or other non-fish predators to get close to prey, mainly small damsel fishes. Widespread Indo-Pacific, and common in the Maldives. Length to 50 cm.
Photos left: Flores, Indonesia.

A group of colourful small fishes that in the Maldives are all planktivores, bottom feeding relatives elsewhere. They are commonly observed by scuba divers and snorkelers. The eye-catching species form large schools when feeding in currents on zooplankton, often well above the reef. Basslets start their adult life as female and males derive from females, usually replacing males that have gone missing. Males are particularly colourful and display with their fins erect, to each other, as well as to females, and often form schools of their own. In many areas females outnumber males, each male dominating a group of females that is known as haremic behaviour. However, most of the Maldives species seems to be an equal sex-ratio.

Threadfin Basslet
Nemanthias carberryi

Clear water reef crests and slopes to about 20 m depth, often in large schools. A very common species in the Maldives with several colour forms that may mimic other basslets or small fusiliers that share the same reef. Highly variable from plain pink-ish with tiny yellow spots all over to partly bright yellow, sometimes a bright red dorsal fin as mimic. Males with two filamentous rays heading the dorsal fin. West Indian Ocean. Length to 12 cm.

Yellow-back Basslet *Pseudanthias bicolor*

Mainly a deep water species found along steep outer reef walls but in the Maldives photographed in 25 m depth that is relatively shallow for this species. Ranges to at least 70 m. Usually forms small groups near caves and often swims inverted inside. Lower half of the body looks blue in natural light. Males with two filamentous rays heading the dorsal fin that have thickened bits at the tips. Widespread Indo-Pacific.
Length to 13 cm. Photo, displaying male: Bali, Indonesia.

Two-spot Basslet *Pseudanthias bimaculatus*

Usually occurs in small groups in current prone areas. Deep water species. Males with dark blotch between 4th and 6th spine of dorsal fin and second, less obvious one at end of fin. Body ornamented with yellow, iridescent blue margins on fins. Females mainly deep-pink with yellow over back and vertical fins. Widespread Indian Ocean, ranging to Bali, Indonesia. Some variations in Indonesia, perhaps subspecies.
Length to 14 cm. Photos: male-left, female-right, by Jörg Aebi.

Yellow-eye Basslet *Pseudanthias* n. sp.

A deep-water dweller found along outer reefs in small groups. It represents a new species, once photographed in Mauritius (female) and now discovered in the Maldives. All photographs taken by Jörg Aebi, at South Màle Atoll. Lenght of male showing orange or yellow saddle-patch below dorsal fin, about 10 cm.

Red Basslet *Pseudanthias cooperi*

Prefers deep slopes and forms schools at remote coral bommies. In the Maldives in small groups, mainly in depths of 30+ m. Juveniles and females dark red, male pales during display and shows dark central bar on body-sides. Moderately common in the Maldives. Widespread Indo-Pacific
Length to 12 cm. Photo: displaying male: Jerry Allen, Mauritius.

Yellow-tail Basslet *Pseudanthias evansi*

Usually forms schools along the upper edge of drop-offs, feeding well away from the reef. Found from near surface waters, when feeding, to about 20 m depth. Often mixed with similar sized yellow backed fusiliers and are easily overlooked in open water. Brightly coloured with pink and yellow, but pink appears blue in natural light. A common Maldives species. Indian Ocean only. Length to 12 cm.

Pink Basslet *Pseudanthias hypselosoma*

In the Maldives mainly deep, usually in 30+ m, with remote coral bommies, but elsewhere often very shallow. Forms small groups and in the Maldives often mixed with Red Basslets. Males have red blotch in dorsal fin that appears black in natural light. West Pacific, ranging into Indian Ocean, as far west as the Maldives. Length to 12 cm. Photo, displaying males: Bali, Indonesia.

Flame Basslet *Pseudanthias ignitis*

Usually swims in schools along the upper edge of drop-offs with tall coral growth to about 15 m depth. Males often display with erected fins intensifying their colours. They have a bright red dorsal fin and red bands over outer rays of caudal fin and body turns yellow. Common in the Maldives Restricted distribution, mainly oceanic, Maldives to Andaman Sea, replaced by sibling *P. dispar* in Pacific. Length to 9 cm. Photo-R: Jörg Aebi.

Short-snout Basslet *Pseudanthias parvirostris*

A small and rarely observed deep water species. Identified by the pink lines on top of the head, from tip of snout to each eye and meeting at beginning of dorsal fin. In the male it continues and thinckens over the back. Originally found in the Philippines at 60 m depth. Also know from Solomon Islands at 35 m. The Maldives fish in lower two photos, a pair, were photographed at 42 m at the base of a large coral head away from the reef, surrounded by course rubble. Length to 65 mm. Top two photos: Jörg Aebi.

Resplendent Basslet *Pseudanthias 'pulcherrimus'*

Mostly found deep along current-prone slopes and drop-offs in depth of 20+ m. Often in large caves, swimming inverted on ceilings. Moderately common in the Maldives but easily overlooked with the similar Orange Basslet that is often abundant in the same habitat. West Indian Ocean only, but seems identical *P. randalli* in Pacific. No original description, but published in Smith's Sea Fishes, Smith & Heemstra, 1986. Length to 65 mm. Photo, male, left: Jörg Aebi.

Orange Basslet *Pseudanthias squamipinnis*

Found in most habitats, from shallow lagoons to deep outer reef walls to at least 40 m. Juveniles and females bright orange. Males turn red with yellow sides and have elongated 3rd dorsal fin spine, latter also in very large females that are likely to change to males in the near future. Very common in the Maldives and often abundant on reef crests. A widespread Indo-Pacific species, but variable with several geographical variations and no doubt several subspecies. Length in the Maldives to 10 cm.

DOTTYBACKS - PSEUDOCHROMIDAE

A large Indo-Pacific family of small, often colourful fishes with at least 6 genera and 70 species, four of which reported from the Maldives. Dividable into sub-families: the PSEUDOPLESIOPINAE are sometimes called Rock Basslets; and PSEUDOCHROMINAE, the dottybacks, 2 of which included here. Many species are cryptic and many were recently discovered, at least two in the Maldives are new, and others can be expected. They are very territorial and aggressive, mostly moving about in the back of caves that provide shelter with narrow crevices. The species are easily identified by their colours, but some are variable and can differ between sexes. Diet comprises various small animals, including other fishes.

Yellow Dottyback *Chlidichthys inornatus*

A common Maldives species living in caves and ledges along steep slopes and drop-offs on inshore reefs. The brightly colour males are easily noticed, but females are usually nearby. Shallow to about 20 m depth. Also known from Sri Lanka and Chagos. Length to 45 mm

Pink-head Dottyback
Pseudoplesiops sp 1

An undetermined species that appears to be new. Found in clear water drop-offs with rich invertebrate growth, swimming in a typical darting style in narrow crevices in depth of 20+ m. Length about 40 mm.

LONGFINS - PLESIOPIDAE

A small Indo-Pacific family with 7 genera and about 20 species as presently defined. Some species, such as mouth-brooders, doubtfully included. Only two species known from the Maldives, but only one commonly seen by divers, included here.

Comet *Calloplesiops altivelis*

Moderately common in the Maldives, but lives secretively in the back of caves or holes amongst boulders, and is usually only noticed when inspecting dark places with a torch. Inshore to outer reefs in depths from 3 to at least 50 m. Easily identified by shape and colour. Widespread Indo-Pacific.
Length to 16 cm, but usually smaller in the Maldives. Photo left: Neville Coleman; right: Jörg Aebi.

TRIPLE TAILS - LOBOTIDAE

Comprises a single genus and species that has a global distribution in tropical seas. Juveniles float below sargassum weed rafts and can be dispersed over great distances.

Triple Tail *Lobotus surinamensis*

Rarely seen in the Maldives by divers and juveniles usually appear during the wet season. Adults in silty habitats, mainly inshore and may enter lower reaches of streams. Juveniles yellowish, mottled, to brown, mimicking leaves, and swim below weed rafts or under debris that originates from land. Adults are drab dark brown to black. Widespread in all tropical seas and occurrence in the Maldives probably fluctuates greatly between wet seasons.
Length to 1 m. Photo, adult: Java, Indonesia; juvenile: Flores, Indonesia.

TRUMPETERS & GRUNTERS - TERAPONTIDAE

Moderately large family with 16 genera and about 40 species, only one known from the Maldives. Trumpeters are usually striped and are primarily marine, but commonly enter estuaries. The grunters are primarily freshwater and the 30 or so species are confined to the Australia - New Guinea region. Some species are caught on lines and typical for the family, make loud grunting noises that are produced with the swimbladder. Diet comprises various small animals, including insects, and some nibble on algae.

Crescent Perch
Terapon jarbua

Inshore species, usually seen in very shallow water, adults swimming in loose groups over sand or mud flats close to beaches or around jetties in harbours. Juveniles intertidal, sometimes entering freshwater. Easily recognised by banded pattern that is similar from juvenile to adult. Length to 25 cm.
Photo: Flores, Indonesia.

FLAGTAILS - KUHLIIDAE

A small family of perch-like fishes, a single genus presently recognised with about 6 species, including one in the Atlantic, and one of which found in the Maldives. Coastal fishes, congregating in surface waters around reef outcrops in surge zones during the day. Feed in open water on zooplankton at night.

Flagtail *Kuhlia mugil*

Flagtails school in surface waters in turbulent zones, usually around reef outcrops that break the surface. Juveniles are more intertidal. Not commonly observed by divers. Usually seen when diving from the shore during entering or leaving the water. Widespread Indo-Pacific, ranging to sub-tropical waters.
Length to 20 cm in tropical waters, larger in cooler zones. Aquarium photo.

BIGEYES - PRIACANTHIDAE

A small family with 4 genera and about 17 species globally in tropical and sub-tropical water, 2 of which known from the Maldives. They are easily recognised by their large eyes, shape and colour. Nocturnal fishes that feed in open water at night, capturing relatively small creatures in the zooplankton with their large mouth.

Crescent-tail Bigeye
Priacanthus hamrur

During the day found in sheltered parts of reefs or in deep lagoons, sometimes swimming more openly about when forming schools. Best identified by the shape of the tail. Colour variably from silvery-pink to red, sometimes with dusky bands that can be turned off at will. Occurs in depths between 10 and 100 m. Widespread and usually common Indo-Pacific. Length to 45 cm.

Glass-eye
Priacanthus blochii

Occurs on protected reefs and in lagoons. Known depth range is 3 to 30 m, but in the Maldives probably extends much deeper. Very similar to *P. hamrur*, but readily identified by rounded caudal fin. Widespread Indo-Pacific.
Length to 30 cm.
Photo: Jörg Aebi.

Blotched Bigeye *Heteropriacanthus cruentatus*

Secretive in reefs during the day, usually moderately deep. Tail with rounded corners and body with blotched pattern. Floats above reefs at night to catch zooplankton. Observed from 3 to 30 m depth. Widespread Indo-Pacific and also Atlantic, ranging into sub-tropical waters.
Length to 32 cm. Photo: Sulawesi, Indonesia.

CARDINALFISHES - APOGONIDAE

A very large family of mostly small fishes in tropical and sub-tropical seas with at least 26 genera and probably well over 250 species globally. Many species are still undescribed and with many similar species there is confusion about the application of names. At least 40 species occur in the Maldives and no doubt more will be found. Habitats range from estuaries (few enter freshwater) to deep off-shore. Cardinalfishes are nocturnal but may feed on plankton during the day, and some juveniles mainly feed during the day. Several species form schools during the day that shelter from current in the protection of reefs. At night they disperse away from reefs and feed in open water, some drifting near the bottom and others feed high in the water column. Many species are extremely secretive and only seen at night, some of which only in the back of dark caves. Females are usually more colourful than males and courts the male during spawning, and the male takes the eggs in the mouth to incubate. Diet comprises various small animals and some prey on fishes.

Photos left, males *Cheilodipterus macrodon* with brood in mouth.
Lower photo: Bali, Indonesia.

Tiger Cardinalfish
Cheilodipterus macrodon

Sheltered reef slopes and large coral heads in lagoons, usually sheltering below overhangs or in small caves. Occurs singly, in pairs or in small loose groups. Shallow to about 30 m depth and generally common throughout the Indo-Pacific range.
Length to at least 22 cm, some Maldives fish appear particularly large compared to elsewhere.

Arrow-tooth Cardinalfish *Cheilodipterus artus*

In the Maldives this species is found mainly in the back of large caves along inner reef walls in 10 to 35 m depth, sometimes in small loose groups. Elsewhere also occur in shallow lagoons under jetties or in staghorn corals, often forming large dense schools. Widespread Indo-Pacific. Length to 12 cm.

Toothy Cardinalfish *Cheilodipterus isostigma*

Common in the Maldives, especially in deep lagoons amongst staghorn corals in 10 to 15 m depth. Juveniles occur solitary, adults in pairs, usually several present and each pair protecting its territory during the day. Nearly identical to *C. quinquelineatus,* but body stripes thinner and snout appears slightly longer. Appears to be widespread Indo-Pacific. Length to 11 cm.

Five-line Cardinalfish
Cheilodipterus quinquelineatus

Mainly found along inner reef margins, forming small groups below overhangs over sand or well protected spaces between large coral heads. Usually to 15 m depth, but occasionally deeper on outer reef. Widespread and generally common throughout Indo-Pacific. Length to 10 cm.

Narrow-striped Cardinalfish
Apogon angustatus

A common shallow water species, mainly on reef crests in 6 to 15 m depth. Has a distinctive tail fin base spot that finishes the mid-body stripe. Widespread Indo-Pacific.
Length to 11 cm.

Black-striped Cardinalfish *Apogon nigrofasciatus*

A common species in caves and crevices on steep slopes and drop-offs. Occurs singly or in pairs in depths from 6 to 40 m. There are two forms, differentiated by yellow or white interspaces between the broad black stripes, only the latter found in the Maldives. The former appears to be restricted to Indonesia and the latter widespread Indo-Pacific. Length to 10 cm.

Copper-striped Cardinalfish
Apogon holotaenia

Photographed in the Maldives for the first time in 35 m depth. A pair was found on open sand and rubble bottom, sheltering with small coral outcrops on sand. Known from the western Indian Ocean, usually reported as coastal and shallow habitat. Reports from Pacific locations probably based on similar species.
Length to 8 cm.

Pearly-lined Cardinalfish
Apogon taeniophorus

Normally found intertidal on sheltered reef crest under large loose coral pieces, rarely deeper than 10 m. Originally named from the Maldives. Several similar species, best recognised by the partially thickened lower stripe. Widespread Indo-Pacific.
Length to 10 cm. Flores, Indonesia.

Short-striped Cardinalfish
Apogon sp 1

Only one pair found at Maalhoss in Baa Atoll in 42 m depth. Large rubble pieces overgrown with coralline algae at the base of a remote coral head provided coverage. Very similar to *A. franssedai* from Indonesia that lives at comparable depths but in large caves.
Length about 55 mm.

Plain Cardinalfish
Apogon apogonides

Commonly found around deep coral out-crops on sand flats. Usually just away from main reefs, in depths of about 30 m. Juveniles may be shallower. Forms small groups during the day. Plainly coloured and only adults show some colours on the head. Widespread Indo-Pacific. Length to 10 cm.

Maldives Cardinalfish
Apogon sp 2

An undescribed species only known from the Maldives. It is closely related to *A. properuptus* from Australia and Indonesia, and has been misidentified as *A. cyanosoma*. A common species in lagoons and harbours, often in groups consisting of pairs. Shallow to about 20 m depth.
Length to 7 cm.

Spiny-head Cardinalfish *Apogon kallopterus*

Common in the Maldives, usually on sheltered spots near surge areas on outer and inner reefs. Forms small groups during the day. Highly variable in colour, juveniles usually with a thick black stripe and large black spot on caudal fin base that is just above centre. The stripe and spot can completely disappear in large adults, but these can be distinguished by the yellow first dorsal-fin. Widespread Indo-Pacific. Length to 15 cm.

Spiny-eye Cardinalfish *Apogon freanatus*

Various reef habitats, usually seen in depths between 6 and 25 m. In small groups during the day, usually sheltering below reef-overhangs over sand. Disperses at night, swimming low over open sand-flats. Identified by the thick mid-lateral stripe, tapering at the end, followed by a large spot at same level on the tail base. Some variations and sometimes stripe faded to barely a trace. Generally common and widespread Indo-Pacific. Length to 10 cm.

Tapered-line Cardinalfish
Apogon exostigma

Very common in the Maldives in sandy lagoons in about 10 m depth. Seems to prefer large corals of the species shown in the background of the photographs. Many pairs share such habitat, but they are territorial and disputes are common when space is limited. Identified by the pale colour and tapering mid-lateral stripe. With or without caudal-fin base-spot, when present at level just above stripe. The spotless form is often referred to as *A. abrogramma*, now appears to be a junior synonym. The spot on *A. exostigma* in the Maldives is normally present in the morning but fades in the afternoon, and absent at night as shown in lower photograph. Widespread Indo-Pacific.
Length to 12 cm.

Big-eye Dusky-cardinalfish
Apogon cf savayensis

Appears to be very common in the Maldives. Usually in large coral heads on the bottom of sandy lagoons about 10 m deep. Not too secretive and easily seen during the day in narrow crevices. Out at night over sand and rubble. A dusky looking fish with indistinct barring on sides; black saddle on caudal fin-base that quickly fades below lateral line; broad black leading margins on dorsal fins. Widespread Indo-Pacific.
A small species, to 8 cm long.

Barred Dusky-cardinalfish
Apogon cf bandanensis

Sheltered lagoons with rich coral growth. Forms small groups during the day that can be seen inside branching corals. One of the few dusky species seen during the daytime. Possibly widespread Indo-Pacific, but various forms may represent different species. Length to 65 mm.

Clear-finned Dusky-cardinalfish
Apogon cf fuscus

Very secretive in reefs, often in narrow crevices in the back of caves and usually hiding from view. Mainly clear coastal drop-offs to outer reefs to depths of about 25 m. Comes out at night but swims close to the reef. Distinguished by plain fins. Widespread Indo-Pacific. Length to 10 cm. Photo: Toshikazu Kozawa.

Yellow-edged Cardinalfish *Apogon* sp 3

Moderately common in the Maldives but usually only seen at night when swimming above corals. Has yellow edges on the last three fins. Sheltered reefs with rich coral growth, hiding at the base of dense branching corals during the day. In the process of being described. Widespread Indo-Pacific. Length to 10 cm.

Grey-ring Cardinalfish
Apogon sp 4

Lagoon, rubble-reef slopes to 10 m depth. Undetermined species that is similar to *A. annularis* from the Red Sea. One of a group that typically are dusky coloured, have a angular line below the eye and a dark spot or bar on the base of the tail, perhaps 7 similar species involved. Secretive in reefs but can be found in sheltered reefs during the day. Floats above reef at night. Length to 10 cm.

Cave Cardinalfish *Apogon evermanni*

Lives inverted on the ceiling of large caves and can be found during the day. More often noticed at night when a torch is used. Common in the Maldives between 6 and 35 m depth but reported to 70 m. Easily recognised by distinctive colouration. Widespread Indo-Pacific and also Atlantic, most widespread cardinalfish. Length to 12 cm. Shown as photographed.

Night Cardinalfish
Apogon doryssa

Commonly found on night dives along steep slopes and drop-offs, swimming in the shelter of caves and ledges. Some pearly spots above the head distinguished this species from similar ones that could occur in the Maldives. Widespread Indo-Pacific. Length to 50 mm.

Long-spine Cardinalfish *Apogon leptacanthus*

Occurs in schools amongst corals or in holes in rubble piles in lagoons and harbours during the day. Moves out separately over sand, feeding close to the sand on small shrimps. Adults identified by tall first dorsal fin. Widespread Indo-Pacific. Length to 60 mm.

Gilbert's Cardinalfish *Apogon gilberti*

Shallow Lagoons and harbours, in staghorn coral or rubble walls in holes. Often mixed with other species, best distinguished by the black spot near the tail and black tips on the tail fin. Previously only known from the West Pacific, this is first record for the Maldives. Length to 45 mm.

Sangi Cardinalfish
Apogon sangiensis

Sheltered sand slopes and harbours, usually with remote outcrops of dead coral on sand or large anemone to about 20 m depth. Identified by a small black spot at end of base of each dorsal fin. Photographed in Male Harbour, first record for the Maldives. Widespread Indo-Pacific.
Length to 8 cm.

Harbour Cardinalfish *Foa fo*

Sheltered habitat from coastal silty bays to deep off shore soft bottom to at least 50 m depth. Found with soft corals, weeds and sponges during the day, and occasionally under the mantle of large anemones. Widespread Indo-Pacific, previously included with *F. brachygramma* a Hawaiian species.
Length to 45 mm.
Photo: Flores, Indonesia.

Elat Cardinalfish *Foa abocellata*

A small secretive species that can be found on the bottom at night on reefs or sand close by, hunting small prey. Easily overlooked and probably mistaken for a juvenile of something else. Known from 6 to 25 m depth. Indian Ocean, ranging to Bali. Replaced by *F. ahimsa* in Pacific. Length to 5 cm. Previously wrongly placed in *Fowleria* and is most similar to *Foa*.

Variegated Cardinalfish
Fowleria variegata

Coastal shallow reefs and harbours in rubble or dead coral pieces. Rarely seen unless disturbing the bottom or diving in silty habitats at night. Colour variable from brown to near black with mottled pattern. Widespread Indo-Pacific.
Length to 8 cm.
Photo: Australia.

Cross-eyed Cardinalfish
Fowleria aurita

Coastal and inner reefs from intertidal to about 20 m depth, usually in dense reefs comprising mostly rubble with mixed algae and coral cover. Secretive and even at night usually seen in small passages or holes. Widespread Indo-Pacific.
Length to 9 cm.
Photo: Flores, Indonesia.

Peppered Cardinalfish
Fowleria punctulata

Common in the Maldives but secretive and usually in very shallow protected reef habitats from intertidal to about 10 m depth. Colour pale to reddish brown and distinctive spots on the body distinguishes this species from similar ones. Widespread Indo-Pacific.
Length to 9 cm.
Photo: Australia.

Painted Cardinalfish
Archamia fucata

Various habitats in lagoons with rich coral growth or separate large coral patches remotely on sand. Forms schools during the day. Highly variable in colour in relation to surroundings: ranging from plain, near white, to strongly lined with orange. Patchy occurrence in the Maldives. Widespread Indo-Pacific.
Length to 10 cm.

Nose-spot Cardinalfish
Rhabdamia cypselura

Forms large and dense schools during the day. Usually found in sheltered parts of reefs or on the side of large remote coral heads on deep sand flats, to 50 m. Sometimes small groups are found in caves. Best recognised by the semi-translucent brown or yellow colour and dark spots on the snout. Widespread Indo-Pacific.
Length to 55 mm.
Photo: Bali, Indonesia.

Slender Cardinalfish
Rhabdamia gracilis

Translucent white and silvery on abdomen and has black tips on the tail fin. Forms small schools during the day, usually near coral bommies in depths over 10 m, but drift individually above reefs or over sand at night to feed on zooplankton. Widespread Indo-Pacific, usually common but not often seen in the Maldives.
Length to 6 cm.
Photo: Flores, Indonesia.

Black-tail Cardinalfish
Pseudamia hayashii

Nocturnal and even during the night in the back of far reaching large caves. Tail fin usually darker than body and black in juveniles. Known from scattered localities in the Indo-Pacific, first record for the Maldives. Photographed in a large cave at 25 m depth and was locally common.
Length to about 65 mm seen, reported to 10 cm.

Tail-spot Cardinalfish *Pseudamia gelatinosa*

Only seen at night, usually on open sand slopes with small reef outcrops, swimming just above the bottom. Sinks to the bottom when in the light of a torch, as shown in the photograph. Tail with about eye-size spots on base and upper part of fin, usually distinct in adults that has lighter fin. Widespread Indo-Pacific. Length to 11 cm. Photo, fish on bottom: Bali, Indonesia.

TILEFISHES - MALACANTHIDAE

A small tropical family with 2 genera and about 10 species, only one known from Atlantic seas, and at least 4 occur in the Maldives. The tilefishes live in relatively deep water and only two, commonly known as blanquillos, enter shallow depths. Adults often pair and many are nest builders, making large seamounts in deep water. They feed on various small bottom creatures.

Flagtail Blanquillo
Malacanthus brevirostris

Usually fairly deep in the Maldives in 20+ m on open sand flats near low reefs or rubble patches. Digs holes under solid pieces for shelter and nesting. Occurs singly or in pairs. Post-larvae large, about 75 mm long. Widespread and often common in the Indo-Pacific.
Length to 30 cm, usually about 20 cm.

 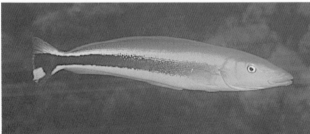

Blue Blanquillo *Malacanthus latovittatus*

Large adults swim above rubble flats of reefs or along reef bases and sand channels between reefs. Juveniles occur low on the bottom on small sand patches in reefs and have a colour pattern similar to some juvenile wrasses that appears to work as a deterrent to predators. Adults enter shallow reef flats but more commonly seen in 20 or more metres depth. Widespread Indo-Pacific.
Length to 35 cm. Photo left, small juvenile: Flores, Indonesia.

Green Tilefish
Hoplolatilus cuniculus

Uncommon but usually occurs in numerous pairs where found. Deep water and a large population was found at Kagi. A rather plane species, greenish to light brown. Widespread Indo-Pacific, usually over 30 m depth.
Length to 15 cm.

Blue-saddle Tilefish
Hoplolatilus sp 1

An undetermined species that was seen by the author in the same area as the Green Tilefish. The tail looked black at that depth. The blue markings suggest that this species is closely related to the Pacific species, its sibling, *H. fronticinctus,* and appears to undescribed. It was recently photographed in Bali by Takamasa Tonozuka, and probably occurs widespread Indian Ocean.
Length about 16 cm.
Photographs: South Malé Atoll, by Jörg Aebi.

Blue Tilefish
Hoplolatilus sp 2

This briliantly blue species was only recently found in the Maldives by the photographer, but it was recently photographed in Bali by Takamasa Tonozuka. An undetermined species and appears to be undescribed, and probably occurs throughout the Indian Ocean. It is similar to species such as *H. chlupatyi* from the Pacific and maybe its sibling. Like most species in the genus, it has a preference for deep water and occurs on open rubble-bottom habitat.
Length about 12 cm.
Photographs: South Malé Atoll, by Jörg Aebi.

REMORAS - ECHENEIDAE

Small family with 4 genera and 8 species, all with global distribution in tropical and temperate seas, 4 of which reported from the Maldives. Two are particularly common and included here. They feature a sucker disc on top to the head that has evolved from the spinous fin into series of laminae. They hitch rides on all kinds of oceanic creatures, including sharks, rays, turtles, large fishes etc. Diet comprises scraps from their feeding host and some species take parasites off their host.

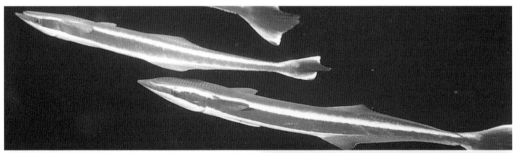

Slender Suckerfish
Echeneis naucrates

The most common and most observed species by divers in tropical seas, occurring in almost every marine habitat from estuaries to oceanic. Juveniles can be found on many reef fishes and often swim by themselves in small groups. Adults too, are often seen without host and may even try to hitch a ride with a diver. Usually identified by the broad black mid-body stripe, but this may fade in large individuals.
Length to 1 m.
Photos: Bali, Indonesia. Lower shows ventral parts.

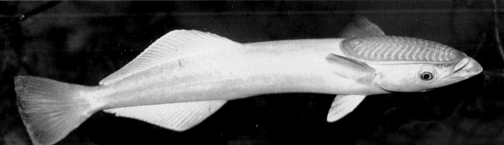

Short Suckerfish
Remora remora

Usually only seen attached to large sharks, and is primarily an oceanic species that occasionally is carried inshore by their host. A rather stocky and plain looking species, pinkish grey. Disk very large. Widespread and ranging into temperate seas.
Length to 80 cm in temperate seas, usually smaller in tropical waters.
Photos: Australia, lower shows disk in detail.

JACKS & TREVALLIES - CARANGIDAE

Large tropical to warm-temperate family with approximately 25 genera and 140 species, and about 20 species are known from the Maldives. They are primarily pelagic and this number will probably increase in time, as many migrate. Streamlined silvery fishes with smooth skin, featuring a series of bony scales along tail, called scutes. They are fast swimming hunters, the smaller species taking zooplankton and larger ones taking smaller fishes. However, in turn all are hunted by the larger tunas or dolphins and targeted by people. Many species swim close to reefs, preying on those making mistakes when being distracted or swimming too far from safety. Generally juveniles and small species school in shallow depths, and the larger species hunt solitary or in small groups in a great depth range.

Big-eye Trevally *Caranx sexfasciatus*

A large and common species, singly, in small groups and sometimes in large schools along deep drop-offs. Often shows interest in divers. Juveniles inshore, including mangroves. Adults rather elongated compared to similar species and eye large. Widespread Indo-Pacific.
Length to 85 cm. Photo, juvenile: Jörg Aebi.

Giant Trevally *Caranx ignobilis*

Largest trevally, giants often seen solitary along deep slopes but occasionally in small groups or schools in outer reef channels. Juveniles inshore, often hunting close to beaches. Widespread Indo-Pacific.
Length to 1.7 m. Photo, adult: Java, Indonesia.

Blue-fin Jack
Caranx melampygus

Commonly seen patrolling reef slopes, often swimming near bottom feeders that disturb other fishes targeted by the jack. Occasionally in schools along outer reef walls. A robust species as adult. Widespread Indo-Pacific.
Length usually to 70 cm, reported to 1 m.

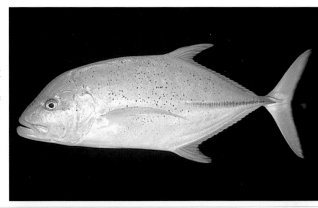

Black Jack
Caranx lugubris

Clear coastal slopes and outer reef drop-offs. Usually solitary or in small numbers swimming close to reefs in moderate depths over 15 m. A dark looking species with a long streak of black scutes along the tail. Widespread in all tropical seas.
Length to 80 cm.

Blue-spined Trevally
Carangoides caeruleopinnatus

A deep bodied species found on inner reefs and in lagoons. Often occurs in silty habitat, along slopes or near large remote coral bommies. Juveniles solitary, adults often in pairs. Variable in colour, juveniles strongly banded, developing numerous yellow spots over the body with age. Widespread Indo-Pacific.
Length to 40 cm. Photo: Flores, Indonesia.

Banded Trevally
Carangoides ferdau

Mainly found on sand slopes or along the bases to about 20 m deep. Occurs singly or in small groups, occasionally forms schools along deep drop-offs. Swims fast and low over the bottom to hunt. prey. Sometimes follows other species that disturb the bottom. Small juveniles yellow with dark band and often swim with jellies. Widespread Indo-Pacific.
Length to 70 cm.

Yellow-spotted Trevally
Carangoides fulvoguttatus

Adults primarily in deep water, usually seen in small groups well away from reefs above open sandy bottom, entering deep lagoons. Greenish above and usually some scattered small black spots on the upper sides, large individuals often with several larger spots centrally along the tail. Widespread Indo-Pacific.
Length to 90 cm.
Photo: Java, Indonesia.

Island Trevally
Carangoides orthogrammus

Know as Thicklip Trevally elsewhere. Adults with blue fins, the tip of the dorsal fin rather long. Body with yellow spots scattered over the sides. Usually seen solitary in the vicinity of deep water, along drop-offs or deep sand flats visiting large coral bommies. Widespread Indo-Pacific.
Length to 60 cm.
Photo: Neville Coleman.

Bar-cheek Trevally
Carangoides plagiotaenia

An inshore species, usually found in moderately deep water along slopes or with shipwrecks. Often swims well away from reefs in current channels to hunt reef dwellers planktivores such as fusiliers or basslets. Usually seen solitary, but sometimes in small loose aggregations. Widespread Indo-Pacific.
Length to 45 cm. Photo: Flores, Indonesia.

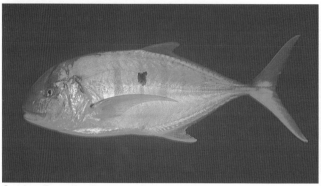

Golden Trevally *Gnathanodon speciosus*

Juveniles and semi-adults often seen with large pelagic fish acting as pilot fishes, but also have been seen with turtles and even seasnakes. The distinctive yellow and black barred pattern remains to almost adult size. Adults live in deep water where forming schools and swim over open bottom that stretches between distant reefs. Widespread Indo-Pacific. Length to 1 m. Photo, adult: Jörg Aebi; juvenile: Japan.

Pilot Fish *Naucrates ductor*

Pelagic species, usually seen swimming near the head of sharks or other large pelagics to feed on scraps. Juveniles often seen with jellies or below floating object off-shore, sometimes blown inshore. Widespread in all tropical seas, sometimes ranging into warm-temperate zones.
Length to 70 cm. Photo: Australia.

Rainbow Runner
Elagatis bipinnulata

A common pelagic species in the Maldives. Occasionally visits reefs or enters deep lagoons. Swims in small to moderately sized schools in surface waters as well as deep in pursuit of food. Diet comprises mainly fishes but also takes the large zooplankton creatures that usually swim deep. Found in all tropical seas.
Length to 1.2 m.

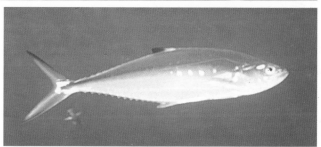

Double-spotted Queenfish
Scomberoides lysan

A common pelagic. Usually seen solitary, swimming just below the surface along beaches and deep side of reef crests, often patrolling the same area on a regular basis. Sometimes in groups and reported to depths of 100 m. Widespread Indo-Pacific.
Length to 70 cm.
Photos: Bali, Indonesia.

Big-eye Scad
Selar crumenophthalmus

A schooling species, often gathering in large numbers in sheltered inshore bays. Feeds primarily on zooplankton and has been recorded to depths in excess of 150 m. Generally a common species in tropical seas in coastal waters as well as islands in all tropical seas.
Length reported to 35 cm, usually less than 25 cm.
Photo: Java, Indonesia.

Mackerel Scad
Decapterus macarellus

A schooling pelagic, common in the Maldives. Swims in tight groups in pursuit of zooplankton. Occurs in various depths along reefs from near surface to almost 200 m depth. A slender species, showing a blue line along side in natural light and a small black 'ear' spot. Widespread in all tropical seas.
Length to 32 cm.

Black-spotted Pompano
Trachinotus baillonii

Very common in the Maldives. Often seen in shallow waters near beaches, but also in current channels at lagoon entrances and outer reefs where swimming near the surface. Identified by the slender shape and series of pupil-sized spots along the sides. Widespread Indo-Pacific.
Length to 56 cm.

Snub-nose Pompano
Trachinotus blochii

Large adults usually seen solitary in deep water around reefs. Juveniles swim in small schools along sandy beaches in very shallow depth, sometimes viewed in small waves rolling onto the beach. Deep bodied, juveniles with bright yellow fins, becoming dull in adults. Widespread Indo-Pacific.
Length to 65 cm.
Photo lower, juvenile: Neville Coleman.

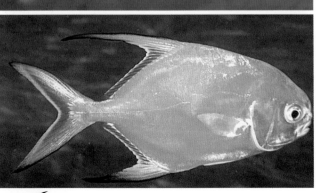

SILVER BATFISHES - MONODACTYLIDAE

Small Indo-Pacific family with 3 genera and about 5 species, only one of which in the Maldives. Deep-bodied reflective, silvery fishes. The ventral fin is greatly reduced or rudimentary in some adults. Juveniles mainly estuarine and some species can live in freshwater. Diet comprises plankton and floating algae.

Silver Batfish
Monodactylus argenteus

A common mainland species that occurs sporadic in the Maldives. A schooling shallow water fish that occurs in protected lagoons, usually found near the mouth of rivers in other areas. Widespread Indo-Pacific.
Length to 12 cm.
Photo: Charles Anderson.

PURSEMOUTHS - GERREIDAE

Moderately sized tropical to warm-temperate family with 7 genera and an estimated 40 species, 4 of which known from the Maldives. They are called silverbellies or silverbiddies elsewhere and mojarras in America. Silvery, deep bodied fishes with a greatly expandable mouth. Bottom feeders, usually alone or in small loose groups, swimming slowly with sudden stops in search for small invertebrates. Most are shallow water species but may venture into greater depths, some are known to range to at least 50 m depth.

Oblong Pursemouth
Gerres oblongus

Commonly seen on shallow sand flats and slopes, adjacent to reefs and on the bottom of sand lagoons. Usually seen solitary, but others often nearby. This species gets large and is more slender when adult compared to other silver bellies in the area. To depths of about 10 m. Widespread Indo-Pacific.
Length to 30 cm.

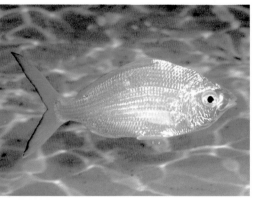

Black-tip Pursemouth *Gerres oyena*

Inshore species, often shallow along beaches and in estuaries, swimming along reef edges with fine rubble and sand. Body rather deep and elevated part of dorsal fin with a dark tip or margin. Widespread Indo-Pacific. Length to 20 cm.

Small-scale Pursemouth
Gerres acinaces

Mainly in clear water sand flats near outer reefs, swimming adjacent to reefs over sparse rubble zones. Usually seen solitary from very shallow to over 20 m depth. Deep bodied and adults with vertical series of dusky spots along upper sides. Widespread Indo-Pacific. Length to 25 cm.

Short Pursemouth
Gerres abbreviatus

Inshore sand flats, entering very shallow depths, often seen in small spread out groups intertidal on high tide. Sheltered bays to about 10 m depth. Deep bodied, lower fins distinctively yellow, and dorsal fin tall with dusky tip. Widespread Indo-Pacific.
Length to 30 cm.
Photo: Flores, Indonesia.

SPINECHEEKS - NEMIPTERIDAE

Moderately large family with 5 genera and at least 64 species, of which only one genus and 3 species known from the Maldives. These fishes swim close to the bottom and pick small prey from rubble and sand with their excellent eye sight. They typically swim a short distance and suddenly stop to study the bottom for any movement of potential prey, diet mostly comprising worms and various small creatures.

Monocle Bream *Scolopsis bilineata*

Usually shallow in clear lagoons and protected reefs to 30 m depth. A common species found on, or near reefs on rubble bottom. Adults occur singly or on pairs, juveniles always solitary. Variable, Maldives fish usually lack yellow stripes, juvenile with similar colours of the venomous *Meiacanthus* blenny, a form of mimicry. Widespread Indo-Pacific, Pacific fish more yellow. Length to 20 cm.

Blue-stripe Spinecheek *Scolopsis xenochroa*

A deep water species in the Maldives, found on sand flats of 25+ m in clear water areas near outer reefs. Usually seen in small groups in rubble sand habitats with invertebrate growth such as seawhips. Colour variable with habitat, pale with little colour on white sand, showing more blue in reef habitat. Mainly west Pacific, ranging as for as the Maldives. Length to 20 cm.

Golden Spinecheek *Scolopsis aurata*

Found in various habitats from silty shallow lagoons to deep sand flats well away from reefs. Usually seen in small loose groups, but form schools in deep water. Schools occasionally enter divable depths to feed near reefs. Indian Ocean, from Maldives ranging east to Java. Length to 23 cm. Photo, darker form: Java, Indonesia.

EMPERORS - LETHRINIDAE

Moderately large Indo-Pacific family with 5 genera and about 40 species, 18 of which reported from the Maldives. Some are restricted to very deep water. Oval-shaped, medium sized fishes, largest to about 1 m long, and important food fishes in some areas. Bottom dwellers, feeding on small invertebrates or worms. Prey is targeted by sight or by taking a mouth-full of sand, in a spot with potential prey, that is filtered through the gills. Some of the larger species prefer feeding at night when adult.

Orange-finned Emperor *Lethrinus erythracanthus*

Usually found on silty lagoon reefs with rich algae on coral bases. A commonly observed species on sheltered inshore reefs and in lagoons. Adults range to 120 m depth. Large adults solitary and easily recognised by the coloured fins that vary from deep yellow to bright orange. Juveniles greenish. Widespread Indo-Pacific. Length to 70 cm, rarely over 50 cm.

Orange-stripe Emperor *Lethrinus obsoletus*

Commonly found in deep lagoons to about 30 m depth. Adults sometimes in small loose groups and often feed in very shallow depth, juveniles on algae reefs. Variable in colour and quickly changes colour with mood from blotchy to pale, with light orange stripe along lower sides. Widespread Indo-Pacific. Length reported to 60 cm, usually 45 cm. Photo, juvenile: Australia.

Yellow-lip Emperor
Lethrinus xanthochilus

Enters sand slopes and flats adjacent to deep water. Adults rather plain and recognised by their slender body and yellow lips. Usually seen solitary but occasionally in small groups. Juveniles inhabit seagrass beds. Widespread Indo-Pacific.
Length to 60 cm.

Black-blotch Emperor *Lethrinus harak*

Inshore species, mainly quite protected waters, including seagrass beds. Often in silty conditions. Small juveniles live amongst seagrasses and occur in mangroves. Usually solitary, but occasionally congregate, probably getting ready to spawn. Usually with distinctive black blotch on side, sometimes with bordering yellow. Widespread Indo-Pacific.
Length reported to 60 cm, usually 40 cm.

Long-nose Emperor
Lethrinus olivaceus

Mainly a schooling species, occasionally seen along deep slopes on inner reefs. Shy in the Maldives. Shallow to deep water, reported to 185 m depth. A large but rather slender species with long snout. Widespread Indo-Pacific.
Length to 1 m. Photo: Scott Michael.

Small-tooth Emperor
Lethrinus microdon

Occurs singly or in small groups on coastal reef slopes, usually at the deeper end. Very similar to the Long-nose Emperor, differing slightly in colour and scale arrangements on the body and is much smaller. Widespread Indo-Pacific. Length to 70 cm, usually to 50 cm.
Photo: Bali, Indonesia.

Spangled Emperor
Lethrinus nebulosus

Adults form small loose groups in deep lagoons. Juveniles in estuaries and often silty habitat with seagrass beds and in deeper areas with sponges. Colour variable, usually yellowish and each scale with a light blue centre. Widespread Indo-Pacific. Length to nearly 1 m.
Photo: Kerama, Japan.

Red-spot Emperor
Lethrinus lentjan

Adults in deep silty habitats, hovering in small groups in reefs shelters during the day to 50 m depth, feeding mainly at night. Juveniles in seagrass beds and active diurnally. Adults are identified by the red spot on their gills at margin. Uncommon in the Maldives, mainly continental coastal waters. Widespread Indo-Pacific. Length to 50 cm, usually much smaller.
Photo: Neville Coleman, Australia.

Blue-line Large-eye Emperor
Gymnocranium grandoculis

Commonly found on sand slopes in protected areas of lagoons, inshore as well as near outer reefs. Swims well above the bottom to hunt invertebrates in the sand. Has excellent eye-sight and can spot prey from a long distance. Large adults develop blue lines on the cheek. Widespread Indo-Pacific.
Length to 50 cm.

Blue-spotted Large-eye Emperor
Gymnocranium microdon

Appears to be this species, not recorded from Maldives before. Deep sandy lagoons, clear water habitat, swimming solitary, several individuals seen in about 15 m depth. Adults develop blue spots over the snout and below front of eye. Widespread Indo-Pacific.
Length to 40 cm.

Large-eye Emperor
Gymnocranium sp

Undetermined species that occurs in large lagoons with good coral growth. Usually swims over rubble and sand along reef margins.
Length to about 45 cm.

Large-eye Bream *Monotaxis grandoculis*

Juveniles in sandy lagoons, swimming just above the bottom in search of prey, along reef sections or over rubble. Adults typically drift in sheltered parts of reef, often near current channels where they congregate during the day. At night the adults feed on various bottom creatures. Widespread Indo-Pacific.
Length to 60 cm.

Gold-spot Emperor
Gnathodentex aurolineatus

A small schooling species, commonly seen along drop-offs or steep slopes from inner to outer reefs. Usually drifting near large caves during the day, dispersing at night to feed on bottom invertebrates. Colour variable from almost silvery to dark brown or grey, identified by the yellow blotch below end of dorsal fin. Widespread Indo-Pacific.
Length to 30 cm.

SWEETLIPS - HAEMULIDAE

Large family with 18 genera and about 120 species, including the sub-family grunts that comprises primarily estuarine species. Sweetlips are represented In the Maldives with 2 genera and 5 species. The greatly thickened lips in adults characterises this group. Juveniles look drastically different from adults and go through several changes with growth in both looks and behaviour. Juveniles are diurnal and adults mainly nocturnal. Diet changes with growth, juveniles feed on algae as well as on zooplankton and tiny mysids, whilst adults hunt various invertebrates and fishes.

Grey Sweetlips
Diagramma sp 1

Adults usually in small groups in deep water along reef edges, sheltering in low reef during the day. Observed in depths of about 40 m. Undetermined species, identical or closely related to *D. labiosum* from Australia. Juveniles are yellowish white and have longitudinal black stripes. Probably widespread Indian Ocean.
Length to almost 1 m.
Photo, blotched adult: Mustag Hussain.

Giant Sweetlips
Plectorhinchus obscurus

Large adults usually found on the upper part of outer reef drop-offs, during the day using large caves. Often swims about openly in adjacent area. Juveniles in coastal waters but rarely seen. Sometimes included with *P. albovittatus* but appears to be incorrect according to Japanese researchers. Widespread Indo-Pacific.
Length to at least 1 m.
Photo, adult side-on: Papua New Guinea; juvenile: Java, Indonesia.

Brown Sweetlips
Plectorhinchus gibbosus

Common in the Maldives, usually on sheltered reefs with large corals for shelter during the day. Singly or in small groups seemingly related to shelter space. Juveniles estuarine. Mainly grey or brownish with indistinct dark barring on the head. Very similar to *P. nigrus* from the Red Sea. Widespread Indo-Pacific.
Length to 75 cm.

Harlequin Sweetlips *Plectorhinchus chaetodonoides*

Also called Spotted Sweetlips. Large adults are commonly seen in caves along inner reef drop-offs. Small juveniles seasonal, occurring in lagoons amongst staghorn corals after wet season. Spotted patterns throughout all stages. Widespread Indo-Pacific.
Length to 60 cm. Photo, juvenile: Flores, Indonesia.

Oriental Sweetlips
Plectorhinchus orientalis

Commonly found in caves along drop-offs on outer reefs, usually in groups. Adults easily recognised by the striped pattern. Juveniles are blotched. Very similar to *P. vittatus* from the Red Sea. Widespread Indo-Pacific.
Length to 50 cm.
Photo above, baby: Toshikazu Kozawa.

SNAPPERS - LUTJANIDAE

A large tropical family with 17 genera and over 100 species globally, 28 of which recorded from the Maldives. Several records doubtful, need to be verified. Some species are only found in very deep waters and not included here. Several sub-families, those commonly seen by divers are the LUT-JANINAE, the benthic snappers that are also the most numerous. Adult fish live in moderate depths, some entering shallow reefs. Juveniles of many species occur inshore, some entering freshwater, often reaching near adult size in shallow depths. Diet comprises invertebrates and fishes, usually taken from the bottom, but some form schools and additionally feed on zooplankton. ETELININAE are the Jobfishes and APSILININAE are the Fusilier Snappers. The latter often mistaken for fusiliers (CAESIONIDAE).

Blue-striped Snapper
Lutjanus kasmira

Usually in depths over 20 m, near deep channels between outer reefs and lagoons. Adults form large schools during the day, sheltering in reefs from strong currents. Juveniles usually in small groups, inshore and often in silty habitats. Easily recognised by the blue lines, but often confused with *L. bengalensis*. Best distinguished by the yellow ventral fins and yellow below the lowest blue stripe. Widespread Indo-Pacific.
Length to 35 cm.

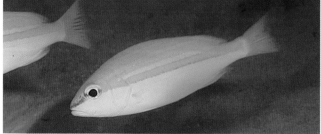

Bengal Snapper
Lutjanus bengalensis

Inshore species, forming small aggregations. Usually in sandy or muddy lagoons around outcrops of dead coral or washed-in land debris. Mostly shallow, rarely deeper than 25 m. Easily overlooked because of the similar colouration to *L. kasmira* and is much less common in the Maldives. More common in continental waters and is widespread Indian Ocean, ranging to Indonesia.
Length to 30 cm, commonly to 20 cm.

Moluccen Snapper
Lutjanus rufolineatus

Forms large dense schools during the day along sheltered coastal reefs between 10 and 30 m where common. Identified by the many yellow horizontal lines and yellow tail. Occurrence in the Maldives needs to be verified. Previously confused with *L. boutton*, another West Pacific species that lacks stripes. A small species, length to 30 cm. Photo: Bali, Indonesia.

Indian Snapper *Lutjanus madras*

Shallow outer reef surge zones in channels and under large coral plates. A flighty species and not commonly seen. Photographed snorkelling at 3 m depth, the only way to get close at the time. Colouration of the Maldives fish is unusual and identification needs to be verified. Mainland fish have thick yellow stripes and lack black side spot. Common along mainland, Sri Lanka to Indonesia and ranging to Philippines. Reported to 90 m depth. Length to 30 cm. Photo, spotless form: Java, Indonesia.

One-spot Snapper
Lutjanus monostigma

Adults shelter in reef during the day, often singly or small groups below short overhangs or caves along walls from about 10 m down. Commonly with ship-wrecks. Hunts on open bottom at night. Recognised by silvery grey body and yellow fins, and usually a small black side spot. Widespread Indo-Pacific. Length to 60 cm.

Black-spot Snapper *Lutjanus erenberghi*

Included here on the basis of literature record and occurrence in the Maldives needs to be verified. A widespread coastal species that is usually found near freshwater run offs, where sometimes in large schools. Possible strays to Maldives in wet season, arriving as post-larvae with floating weeds. Recognised by the large black spot and several thin lines below, running along entire body. Widespread Indo-Pacific. Length to 35 cm. Photo: Flores, Indonesia.

Black-tail Snapper
Lutjanus fulvus

Coastal habitats, adults usually in moderate depths, photograph at 36 m. Juveniles in seagrass and mangrove areas or algae dominated reefs in lagoons, also entering freshwater. Tail and dorsal fins darken with age, black in adults. Widespread Indo-Pacific. Length to 40 cm.

Humpback Snapper *Lutjanus gibbus*

Adults often in dense stationary schools on sheltered inshore reefs, sometimes well above the bottom on slopes. Disperse at night to feed on the bottom. Juveniles mainly in seagrass habitat. Adults have a distinctly concave head profile and very broad upper lobe of the tail fin for which also known as Paddletail. Widespread Indo-Pacific. Length to 50 cm. Photo, adult: Bali, Indonesia.

Mangrove Jack
Lutjanus argentimaculatus

Large adults along deep drop-off between 40 and 120 m. Juveniles and sub-adults inshore, often silty habitat. Small juveniles in estuaries and enter freshwater, forming small aggregations when on reefs. Juveniles are distinctly banded and have red fins when in freshwater, a pattern that is gradually lost with age. Widespread Indo-Pacific. Length to 1.2 m.
Photo, large adult: Guam; others: Flores, Indonesia.

Red Emperor Snapper
Lutjanus sebae

Adults prefer deep water and rarely seen by divers. Juveniles frequently among long-spined urchins. Sub-adults sometimes in small groups in caves at the base of drop-offs or with remote outcrops of reef on deep sand flats in 15+ m depth. Large adults uniformly red. Widespread Indo-Pacific.
Length to 1 m.
Photo, sub-adult: Australia.

Red Bass
Lutjanus bohar

Occurs along reef edges from sheltered inshore habitat to outer reef walls to about 70 m depth. Adults often in small groups, occasionally in schools. Juveniles solitary in lagoons, often with large staghorn coral patches on sand in few metres depth. Small juveniles sometimes mistaken for damselfishes. Common in the Maldives. Widespread Indo-Pacific.
Length to 80 cm.

Two-spot Snapper
Lutjanus biguttatus

Sheltered in shore reefs and in large lagoons with rich coral growth. Solitary or forming schools, slowly swimming low above the corals during the day. Disperses at night, usually swimming well above the bottom, which suggest feeding on zooplankton or mid-water fishes. Recognised by elongated shape and twin white spots. Occurs in West Pacific from New Guinea to Philippines and west to the Maldives.
Length to 20 cm.
Photo, juveniles above: Flores, Indonesia.

Midnight Snapper
Macolor macularis

Protected reef slopes and walls with rich coral growth. Adults in caves or swim openly about and sometimes congregate in loose numbers in reef channels. Juveniles recognised by the very long fins below and swim with feather stars, long-spined urchins and coral fans between 5 and 20 m. Widespread Indo-Pacific. Length to 60 cm.
Photo, adult: Bali, Indonesia.

Black Snapper
Macolor niger

Large adults often in small schools near reef channels adjacent to deep water. Small juveniles solitary, swimming openly about, but close to reefs with rich coral growth. Often confused with *M. macularis*, but juveniles have short fins and adults lack the yellow iris of the other species, and are plain grey to almost black. Common in the Maldives. Widespread Indo-Pacific.
Length to 60 cm.
Photo, small juvenile: Bali, Indonesia.

Green Jobfish *Aprion virescens*

Swims high in the water column over open bottom or at distance along reefs. Usually hunts solitary for fishes and squid, including larger zooplankton animals. Recognised by elongated body, rounded head with eyes placed well back, and very large tail fin. Widespread Indo-Pacific. Length to 1 m. Photo right: Flores, Indonesia.

Small-tooth Jobfish *Aphareus furca*

Commonly seen solitary, occasionally in small groups, swimming close to reefs on inner and outer reefs to depths of about 70 m. Hunts fishes and invertebrates. A fork-tail species, edges of gill plates dusky, showing a two vertical bars, and adults sometimes bright yellow over the top of the snout. Widespread Indo-Pacific. Length to 40 cm.

Fusilier Snapper *Paracaesio sordidus*

Usually seen along deep drop-offs but easily overlooked by lack of colour . Depth range reported between 100 and 200 m, but rises to near surface to feed. Photographed in 20 m depth. Caudal fin very large, reddish but looks dark grey with depth and the fish is well camouflaged against open water. Widespread Indo-Pacific. Length to 40 cm. Photo: Flores, Indonesia.

FUSILIERS - CAESIONIDAE

Moderately sized tropical family with 4 genera and about 20 species, 14 of which known from the Maldives. In many areas the fusiliers form large schools and are a large component of the open water reef species, particularly in the Maldives. The fusiliers are predominantly blue and yellow in colour, forming longitudinal patterns. At night these colours change completely and species resting in crevices may turn red. All are planktivores that congregate in current areas along deep drop-offs, tidal channels and submerged reefs, feeding at any depth where plankton is carried.

Thin-lined Fusilier
Caesio varilineata

A very common species in the Maldives that schools over inner and outer reef flats. Often seen from boats as a stream of blue goes by below. Identified by the thin yellow lines, running parallel along the sides, and lack of black tips on the tail. Widespread Indian Ocean, ranging east to Bali, Indonesia, and Red Sea. Length to 22 cm.

Gold-band Fusilier *Caesio caerulaurea*

Uncommon in the Maldives. Usually in lagoon channels, forming small groups or mixed with other species. A single yellow band along upper sides and dark streaks in the tail fin. Widespread and generally common throughout the Indo-Pacific.
Length to 25 cm.

Moon Fusilier
Caesio lunaris

Common in the Maldives. Occurs in deep lagoons and along inner reefs walls, usually the adults in large schools feeding in various depths from surface waters to 40 m depth. Adults all blue with distinctive black tips on the tail fin. Juveniles have a yellow caudal fin base. Widespread Indo-Pacific.
Length to 35 cm.

Yellow-tail Fusilier
Caesio teres

Not common in the Maldives. Often seen singly in large lagoons and sometimes mixed with other species. Distinguished by the lack of lines or black fin tips, and the yellow mainly confined to the tail area that may extend over the back to the head. Widespread Indo-Pacific, very common in Indonesia.
Length to 20 cm.

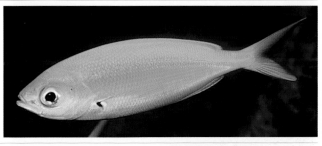

Yellow-back Fusilier
Caesio xanthonota

Common in the Maldives. Forms large schools along inner reefs. Easily recognised by the yellow over the head to tail and lack of black fin tips. Widespread Indian Ocean, ranging to southern Java, Indonesia. Length to 20 cm.

Yellow-banded Fusilier
Pterocaesio sp 1

Uncommon and until now only known from the Maldives and southern Java, no doubt is widespread Indian Ocean. It appears to be closely related to *P. digramma* from the Pacific and seems to be new to science. Only known from outer reef habitats and seamounts.
Length to about 25 cm.
Photo: Java, Indonesia.

Yellow-stripe Fusilier
Pterocaesio chrysozona

Rare in the Maldives, mainly in continental waters of the Indian Ocean. Thick yellow line, running from top of eye to caudal fin, latter with distinct black tips. Widespread Indo-Pacific, mainly common in Indonesia and Australia on inshore reefs. Length to 30 cm. Photo: Bali, Indonesia.

Broad-stripe Fusilier *Pterocaesio lativittata*

Almost identical to *P. chrysozona* but stripe slightly higher on body and lacks black on the base of the pectoral fins. Found in small groups in the Maldives. The Maldives record of another species, *P. tessellata,* appears to be based on a photograph of this species. Reported from Indian Ocean and Papua New Guinea.
Length to 15 cm.
Photo: Christmas Island, Indian Ocean, Roger Steene.

Banana Fusilier
Pterocaesio pisang

Moderately common in lagoon habitats in the Maldives. Variable from plain pale blue to almost red and tail with distinctive black tips. Generally a common widespread Indo-Pacific species, forming small groups along reef slopes and drop-offs, including outer walls.
Length to 16 cm.

Blue-dash Fusilier *Pterocaesio tile*

A common outer reef species, usually forming large schools along deep drop-offs. Recognised by a bright blue dash along the sides that varies in length when seen from different angles. Widespread Indo-Pacific.
Length to 25 cm.

Striped Fusilier
Pterocaesio trilineata

Common in the Maldives but not reported until now. Mainly in silty lagoons and inner reefs, forming moderate sized schools. Easily recognised by the dusky stripes along upper sides. Widespread Indo-Pacific, often common in coastal waters.
Length to 16 cm.

Slender Fusilier *Gymnocaesio gymnoptera*

Appears to be uncommon in the Maldives, but easily overlooked. A small slender species, lacking strong colours and often swims with unrelated similar shaped fishes. Mainly in deep lagoons along reef slopes. Widespread Indo-Pacific, and often on outer reefs in other areas to moderate depths of about 25 m. Length to 15 cm.

Dwarf Fusilier *Dipterygonotus balteatus*

Moderately common, but swims well away from reefs and mainly a schooling pelagic. Often swims with other similar shaped small pelagic fishes and easily overlooked. Widespread Indo-Pacific.
Smallest fusilier, usually not much over 10 cm.

GOATFISHES - MULLIDAE

Moderately large family with 6 genera and at least 50 species, of which at least 10 are found in the Maldives. Readily identified by the pair of barbels below the mouth that are used to probe the bottom for various invertebrates and small fishes. Most species are seen singly or in small groups around reefs but there are several small schooling species that prefer open substrate, often deep silty type bottom, and these are not well known.

Yellow-saddle Goatfish
Parupeneus cyclostomus

Inner and outer reefs from shallow reef crests to moderate depths, reported to 100 m. Adults often seen singly or in pairs, sometimes forms schools. Juveniles bright yellow and in the Maldives the adults commonly retain this colour. Widespread Indo-Pacific,
Length to 38 cm.
Photo, grey form: Bali, Indonesia.

Round-spot Goatfish
Parupeneus pleurostigma

Mainly found in deep water in the Maldives on clean sand flats with rubble and invertebrate rich areas, in 20+ m depth. Easily recognised by the large black spot with a large white area behind. Widespread Indo-Pacific.
Length to 30 cm.
Photo, lower Neville Coleman.

Long-barbel Goatfish
Parupeneus macronema

Common in the Maldives on clear reef crests and slopes on inner as well as outer reefs, usually in small loose groups. Identified by the thick black or red stripe, separated by white area from black tail base spot. Feeds on rubble patches around dead parts of coral bases from near intertidal to about 35 m depth. Widespread Indo-Pacific.
Length to 30 cm.
Photo, lower: Neville Coleman.

Dash-and-Dot Goatfish *Parupeneus barberinus*

Usually found along reefs on sand flats or slopes, usually in depths over 10 m, reported to 100m. Large individuals usually solitary but accompanied by various wrasse species, eager to catch prey that run when the bottom is disturbed by the goatfish. Black stripe usually thin and with yellow above in more colourful specimens. Widespread Indo-Pacific. Length to 40 cm.

Yellow-spot Goatfish
Parupeneus indicus

Appears to be rare in most of the Maldives. Mainly occurs inshore on sheltered reefs with sand zones and in lagoons to about 25 m depth. Easily recognised by the bright yellow spot centrally placed along upper sides. Widespread Indo-Pacific.
Length to 40 cm.
Photo: Bali, Indonesia.

Double-bar Goatfish
Parupeneus bifasciatus

Common in various shallow reef habitats with sand and rubble patches. Adults often seen resting on corals. Young usually in channels on outer reef slopes. The double black band easily identifies this species. Widespread Indo-Pacific, some geographical variations or subspecies.
Length to 30 cm.

Square-spot Goatfish
Mulloidichthys flavolineatus

Common in sheltered lagoons in the Maldives, usually forming active schools around remote large staghorn coral patches on sand. Has small black spot centrally on sides, usually followed by yellow stripe but this is pale in the Maldives due to habitat colour. Spot missing at night. Widespread Indo-Pacific.
Length to 40 cm, but usually much smaller in Maldives.
Photo, upper: Neville Coleman.

Yellow-stripe Goatfish
Mulloidichthys vanicolensis

Schooling species, aggregating during the day in sheltered reefs. Sometimes mixed with blue-striped snapper. Uncommon in Maldives.
Length to 30 cm.
Photo: Charles Anderson.

Schooling Goatfish *Upeneus taeniopterus*

Commonly occurs in silty inshore habitats, seagrass beds and sandy lagoons, usually in schools that move along quickly while feeding. Identified by tail pattern and pale body colour with yellowish line. Widespread Indo-Pacific, mainly oceanic locations. Length to 30 cm.

Shiny Goatfish
Upeneus sp 1

A small species, possibly *U. sundaicus,* that normally has a yellowish stripe along side Stripe may not show because of the white sand habitat in the Maldives, where most fish lack colour. Found in small groups on fine-sand flats in depths over 10 m.
Length about 15 cm.

Bar-tail Goatfish
Upeneus tragula

Reported from the Maldives and appears to be rare here. Usually found in various reef habitats from silty coastal harbours to outer reefs to depths of about 20 m. Found singly or small groups. Widespread and usually common Indo-Pacific.
Length to 30 cm.
Photos: Bali, Indonesia.

BULLSEYES - PEMPHERIDIDAE

Small family with 2 genera and about 20 species globally. Both genera and at least 3 species occur in the Maldives. Nocturnal fishes that school during the day, usually sheltering in caves and some secretive in the back of dark far-reaching caves or tunnels. Distinctive group of fishes by shape, large eyes and small triangular fin on the back, positioned just behind the head and the long anal fin below that reaches the tail fin. They float high above the bottom at night to hunt the larger zooplankton animals.

Greenback Bullseye *Pempheris vanicolensis*

Sheltered inshore wares, harbours and shipwrecks, forming schools where space available. Easily recognised by the black margin on the anal fin and black tip on the top fin. Usually a greenish shiny top, large adults appear reddish brown in natural light. To depths of at least 40 m. Common in the Maldives. Widespread Indo-Pacific. Length to 15 cm.

Silver Bullseye
Pempheris schwenkii

Found mainly along outer reefs in caves. Usually in small groups and often mixes with other species. Fins plain, only dorsal fin with dusky tip. Shiny back, sides yellowish. Occurs in moderate depths, usually between 10 and 50 m. Widespread Indo-Pacific. Length to 15 cm.

Yellow Sweeper
Parapriacanthus ransonneti

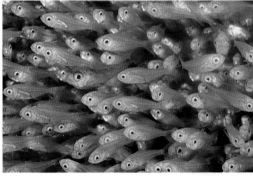

Usually found in large dense schools against reef walls or in caves, and in deep clear lagoons around large remote coral bommies. Easily recognised by its behaviour and yellowish colouration. Often other unrelated species swim amongst them for protection, taking on same colour, such as young cardinal fishes. In depths from 10 to at least 50 m. Widespread Indo-Pacific. Length to 10 cm.

RUDDERFISHES - KYPHOSIDAE

Small family with 3 genera and 10 species globally. Primarily sub-tropical or warm-temperate, but two species occur widespread Indo-Pacific, including the Maldives. They feed primarily on algae and consequently live in shallow waters, often in turbulent high energy zones where food is more abundant. Also known as drummers.

Snubnose Rudderfish
Kyphosus cinerascens

Adults form schools over reefs near tidal channels, or feeding on floating algae at various depth in the currents. Sometimes around shipwrecks to depths of about 30 m. Post larval stages swim under weed rafts and settle in intertidal zones. Recognised by the more elevated fins above and below the tail. Widespread Indo-Pacific. Length to 50 cm.

Brassy Rudderfish
Kyphosus vaigiensis

Inshore reefs with moderate currents, in small groups or schools, often feeding in surface waters along shore lines. Rarely deeper than 10 m. Sometimes shows an evenly spaced pattern of pale blotches over body and head. Widespread Indo-Pacific. Length to 50 cm.

BUTTERFLYFISHES - CHAETODONTIDAE

Large family with 10 genera and about 120 species globally, of which 32 species are known from the Maldives. Many closely related species that are morphologically almost identical. Colouration is often best diagnostic feature. Juveniles can differ considerably in colour from the adult and usually have a much shorter snout proportionally. Diet comprises invertebrates and filamentous algae, most species target small creatures, plankton or pick on corals, and some specialise in particular foods. The plankton feeders may form large schools high above the bottom and the reef-pickers swim in pairs or small groups when adult, staying low on the bottom in search of food. Small juveniles are usually solitary and secretively live in corals or among boulders. Eggs and larvae are pelagic for several weeks. Habitats vary between species from shallow reef flats to deep outer reef walls, but the majority live in relatively shallow depths, rarely below 50 m depth. One species in the Maldives lives very deep: *Prognathodes guyotensis*, usually 100+ m, and is not included here.

Black Pyramid Butterflyfish
Hemitaurichthys zoster

A very common species in the Maldives. Schooling plankton feeder with very distinctive colouration and readily recognised by the broad white and black pattern on the body and head. Often feeds near the surface in large numbers, ranging to a depth of about 30 m. Restricted to western Indian Ocean. Length to 18 cm.

Yellow Teardrop Butterflyfish
Chaetodon interruptus

Found singly or in pairs, occasionally small groups. Differs from the Pacific *C. unimaculatus*, its sibling, in colour. Previously considered a sub-species, but obviously a valid species in its own right. Shallow coral reefs, feeding on small invertebrates, algae and some corals. Western Indian Ocean. Length to 20 cm.

Eclipse Butterflyfish
Chaetodon bennetti

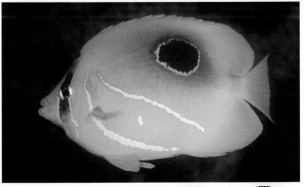

Adults usually swim in pairs close to reefs. Easily recognised from other yellow species by the blue stripes running from the head. Often feeds on coral-like anemones that carpet some reef areas, but also picks on coral polyps. Indo-Pacific. Depth range to about 30 m.
Length to 18 cm.

Racoon Butterflyfish
Chaetodon lunula

Adults usually swim in pairs close to reefs, but occasionally seen floating almost motionless high above reefs in still waters where other reef fishes congregate. Various habitats, feeding on a great variety of invertebrates, to depths of at least 30 m. Widespread Indo-Pacific.
Length to 20 cm.

Yellow Butterflyfish
Chaetodon cf plebeius

Usually seen in pairs, occasionally in small groups, on reefs with rich coral growth to 10 m depth. Feeds mainly on coral polyps. Only known from Indian Ocean, from Maldives to Andaman seas. Previously confused with Blue-dash Butterflyfish *C. plebeius* from the eastern West Pacific and remains an unnamed species.
Length to 15 cm.

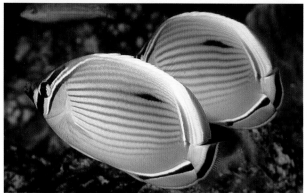

Pinstriped Butterflyfish
Chaetodon trifasciatus

Also called Red-fin or Purple Butterflyfish. Adults swim in pairs or small groups in the shallows of coral rich reefs. Small secretive juveniles in coral thickets. Feeds mainly on coral polyps. Unique colour patterns and obvious orange anal fin. Widespread Indian Ocean, ranging to Bali, Indonesia, replaced by Pacific sibling *C. lunulatus* from Bali on.
Length to 15 cm.

Chevroned Butterflyfish
Chaetodon trifascialis

Typically swims close to large plate-corals (*Acropora*) singly or in pairs, juveniles staying between the branches. Usually to depth of about 15 m, rarely deeper. Identified by chevron lines along body, juvenile with additional black over body at ends of dorsal and anal fins. Widespread Indo-Pacific.
Length to 14 cm.

Brown Butterflyfish
Chaetodon kleinii

Mainly on shallow reef flats and in lagoons but may venture into deep water. Usually forms small groups and lives in various habitats with rich algae growth. Juveniles often mix with small surgeonfishes to feed on algae and small crawling invertebrates. Variable brown to yellow-brown, adults with blue on the nape. Widespread Indo-Pacific.
Length to 12 cm.

Citron Butterflyfish
Chaetodon citrinellus

Shallow reef-flats, including surge zones, lagoons, and harbours, but occasionally seen along deep walls. Usually swims in pairs in the Maldives when adult. Feeds on tiny invertebrates and algae. Identified by pale yellow body with series of dusky to orange dots along scale rows, and black margin on anal fin. Widespread Indo-Pacific.
Length to 11 cm.

Spotted Butterflyfish
Chaetodon guttatissimus

Rich coral growth reefs, often along steep slopes and walls from reef crests to moderate depths in excess of 30 m. Often seen singly or in pairs when adult. Feeds on various small invertebrates, often picking worms from calcareous tubes. Identified by the dense spotting over the body, extending onto dorsal and anal fins. Indian Ocean, ranging to Bali, Indonesia.
Length to 10 cm.

Black-back Butterflyfish
Chaetodon melannotus

Adults usually form pairs in the Maldives. Not particularly common and mainly found in large lagoons with large coral formations to depths of about 20 m. Easily identified by the bright yellow fins, including ventral fins that are white in similar species, and diagonal dark lines over the body. Widespread Indo-Pacific.
Length to 15 cm.

Pig-face Butterflyfish
Chaetodon oxycephalus

Swims in pairs when adult, juveniles secretive among boulders. Often overlooked because of its similarity with the next species that is better known and more widespread. It is best recognised by the broken black band over the eye. Feeds on small invertebrates on the bases of corals, sometimes picking at coral polyps. Indo-Pacific.
Length to 25 cm.

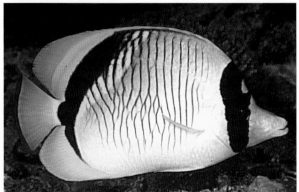

Lined Butterflyfish
Chaetodon lineolatus

Often in reef-channels on outer reefs, feeding on various invertebrates, including anemones and coral polyps. Adults usually in pairs and found in depths of about 10-20 m, but may venture into deep water. Broad black band over the head. Often noticed because of large size. Largest butterflyfish, Indo-Pacific, reported to 45 cm, usually to 30 cm.

Double-saddle Butterflyfish
Chaetodon falcula

Various habitats from lagoons to outer reef walls to 20 m. Adults form pairs, usually seen swimming low on reef. Juveniles solitary and secretive in reefs. Feeds on various invertebrates, including anemones and coral polyps. Easily identified by double black saddle-mark over back. Indian Ocean, replaced by similar *C. ulietensis* in the West Pacific.
Length to 18 cm.

Threadfin Butterflyfish
Chaetodon auriga

Inhabits lagoons and inner reefs, often over sand, feeding on various invertebrates, including tubed or free roaming worms. Adults usually in pairs, juveniles solitary in reefs. Readily identified by areas of diagonal dark lines running opposite ways over the body that end in yellow chevron markings, and adults develop long trailing filament from dorsal fin. Widespread Indo-Pacific.
Length to 24 cm.

Vagabond Butterflyfish
Chaetodon vagabundus

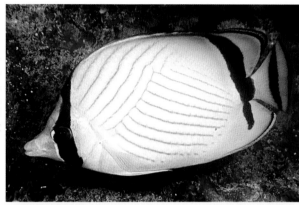

Various habitats and has broad diet range. Rare in the Maldives, usually seen in pairs. Identified by the black banding over the eye, the back of the body and over the tail fin. Dorsal and anal fins end in yellow, compared to black in the similar *C. decussatus* (next species). Widespread Indo-Pacific.
Length to 20 cm.
Photo: Bali, Indonesia.

Blackened Butterflyfish
Chaetodon decussatus

Sometimes called Indian Vagabond Butterflyfish. Readily identified by the large black area covering most of the back part of the dorsal fin and continuing down to the end of the anal fin. Uncommon in the Maldives and mainly seen on shipwrecks, usually in pairs. Common in shallow continental coastal waters. Indian Ocean, ranging east to Flores, Indonesia.
Length to 20 cm.

Head-band Butterflyfish
Chaetodon collare

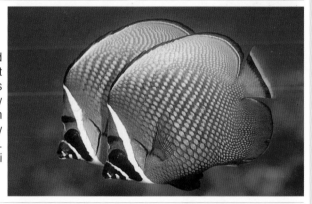

This species is common in the Maldives and occurs in most habitats to depths of at least 35 m. A schooling species but also forms pairs at times, probably when getting ready to spawn. Large schools often congregate on shallow reefs at about 6 m depth. Readily identified by dusky colour and red tail fin. Indian Ocean species, ranging east to Bali where rare.
Length to 18 cm.

Triangular Butterflyfish
Chaetodon triangulum

Mainly on shallow inner reefs with good coral growth but ventures to depths of about 25 m along walls. Common species in the Maldives, adults usually seen in pairs picking on corals, and juveniles among coral branches. Identified by deep body and black tail fin. Indian Ocean species, replaced by the nearly identical *C. baronessa* in the Pacific, both occurring in Java, Indonesia.
Length to 16 cm.

Yellow-head Butterflyfish *Chaetodon xanthocephalus*

Occurs on reefs with good coral growth, usually shallow to about 20 m depth. Adults singly or in pairs. Juveniles on shallow protected reef flats in silty lagoons. Feeds on invertebrates and algae. Adults with rich yellow snout and distinctive colouration on dorsal and anal fins. Closely related to *C. ephippium* and hybrids reported where the two species occur together. West Indian Ocean only. Length to 20 cm.

Meyer's Butterflyfish *Chaetodon meyeri*

Mainly found on reef crests near outer reef walls to depths of about 15 m. Adults swim in pairs and appear to be very territorial, often resulting in fights in areas where common. They are coral nibblers and swim on reefs with rich coral growth. Juveniles solitary and secretive among corals. Easily identified by the purplish body with think diagonal black stripes. Widespread Indo-Pacific, common in the Maldives.
Length to 20 cm. Photo, juvenile: Mustag Hussain.

Ornate Butterflyfish
Chaetodon ornatissimus

Very rare in Maldives and reported from a few but reliable sightings. It is generally common elsewhere in the Indo-Pacific, where it pairs and lives in rich coral growth areas to depths of about 20 m.
Length to 20 cm.
Photo: Bali, Indonesia.

Madagascar Butterflyfish
Chaetodon madagaskariensis

Adults occur singly or in pairs, usually in moderate depths along outer reef walls to at least 50 m. Feeds on a great variety of small mobile invertebrates. Easily identified by the orange band over ends of dorsal and anal fins and chevron lines on the body. One of a complex of several similar species, closely related to *C. mertensii* from the Pacific, but appears to be restricted to the west Indian Ocean.
Length to 12 cm.

Indian Butterflyfish
Chaetodon mitratus

Occurs singly or in pairs in depths below 50 m feeding on various small mobile invertebrates. Rarely shallower, thus not often seen by most divers using compressed air. Readily recognised by the black diagonal bands broadly running from the back and over the eye. It belongs to a complex of similar species of the Indo-Pacific that typically live in depths near the 100 m mark.
Length to 12 cm.
Photo, upper, adult: Jörg Aebi;
Lower, juvenile: Roger Steene, Christmas Island, Indian Ocean.

Long-nose Butterflyfish
Forcipiger flavissimus

Shallow inner reef to upper part of outer reef walls to depths of about 30 m. Nearly always seen in pairs when adult. Picks tiny mobile invertebrates from narrow crevices on reefs and may pick on urchins. Very similar to the next species, but snout shorter and lacks fine dark spotting in the white chest area. Widespread Indo-Pacific.
Length to 22 cm. Photo: Scott Michael.

Very-long-nose Butterflyfish
Forcipiger longirostris

Looks and behaviour similar to previous species, but snout longer and prefers deeper water. Length of snout variable but usually proportionally longer than previous species that looks almost identical. Best distinguished by the fine black spots on the chest near the pectoral fins. Widespread Indo-Pacific.
Length to 22 cm.

Phantom Bannerfish
Heniochus pleurotaenia

Shallow reefs to about 30 m depth. Adults form large schools in the Maldives, but in other parts of the Indian Ocean usually seen in pairs, ranging east to Java, Indonesia. Adults lack banner and is short in juveniles. Identified by mostly brown and black colouration. Replaced by similar *H. varius* in the West Pacific, both occurring in Java where a mixed pair was observed by the author.
Length to 17 cm.

Reef Bannerfish
Heniochus acuminatus

Found singly or in pairs but appears to be uncommon in the Maldives, where mainly found in depths of 20+ metres, and elsewhere often on shallow reefs, ranging to at least 50 m depth. Juveniles coastal and in protected bays. Broad diet. Distinguished from Schooling Bannerfish by slightly longer anal fin and longer snout. Widespread Indo-Pacific.
Length to 25 cm. Photo below: Bali, Indonesia.

Singular Bannerfish
Heniochus singularius

Prefers rich coral growth areas and can be seen in various habitats from shallow reef crests to deep walls. This species normally swims in pairs when adult, but rather rare in the Maldives and often seen singly. Juveniles usually in protected inshore reefs. More elongate than other bannerfish, banner short. Widespread Indo-Pacific.
Length to 30 cm, the largest of the bannerfishes.

Masked Bannerfish
Heniochus monoceros

Often found in caves along deep walls and slopes, shallow to at least 50 m depth. Adults are usually in pairs. Feed on mixed invertebrate and algae diet. Adults best identified by the single black band extending vertically from the ventral fins and belly, ending behind start of short white banner. Widespread Indo-Pacific.
Length to 23 cm.

Schooling Bannerfish
Heniochus diphreutes

Common schooling fish in the Maldives, found in shallow lagoons to deep reef walls, venturing well beyond diving depths. Feeds primarily on plankton but may pick on reefs for food. Juveniles clean other fish from parasites, whilst adults clean on occasion. Has very short snout and anal fin more angular in shape and shorter compared to Reef Bannerfish. Widespread Indo-Pacific.
Length to 20 cm.

ANGELFISHES - POMACANTHIDAE

Large family with 7 genera and over 80 species, of which at least 14 species are known from the Maldives. Some are very rare and more can be expected. The small species are secretive and easily overlooked. They differ from the closely related butterflyfishes in having a clearly visible spine on the lower corner of the gill plates. The large *Pomacanthus* species have juvenile stages that are similar to each other: black with many white lines on the body with electric blue in the fins. They change at almost half adult size to the completely different adult colouration. This change occurs rather quickly as changing forms are rarely seen. The small *Centropyge* species show little change with growth, generally becoming more colourful when adult. Most species feed on mixed algae and invertebrates. Some prefer algae, especially when juvenile, and others may specialise on sponges. Only *Genicanthus* are plankton feeders. Eggs and larvae are pelagic for several weeks, and post-larvae settle in specific habitats that relate to diet. Most species live shallow, some species ranging to about 50 m.

Regal Angelfish
Pygoplites diacanthus

Also called Empress Angelfish in the Maldives. Common on Maldives reefs and although mostly seen solitary, usually occurs in loose groups. Small juveniles live secretively in caves. Feeds primarily on sponges and found on most reefs from shallow crests to almost 80 m. Widespread Indo-Pacific, but two forms between Indian and Pacific Oceans, difference especially noticeably on the head that is grey in the Pacific and orange in the Indian Ocean. Length to 25 cm.
Lower left picture is a rare colour variation.

Three-spot Angelfish *Apolemichthys trimaculatus*

Adults occur solitary or in small groups on reef crests and slopes to about 30 m depth, but mostly shallow in the Maldives. Small juveniles usually on deep slopes. Adults readily identified by the bright yellow colour and blue lips. Small juveniles all yellow with black line over head and distinctive black spot towards the back. Feeds on ascidians, sponges and algae. Widespread Indo-Pacific.
Length to 26 cm. Photo, small juvenile: Mabul, Malaysia.

Smoke Angelfish
Apolemichthys xanthurus

Also called Yellowtail Angelfish, but this name applies to several other angelfishes. Adults usually seen in pairs when deep but singly in shallow part of depth range where less common. Seems to prefer depths over 30 m with open flat reef and low ledges with sponge and soft coral growth. Recognised by the blackened fins, followed by yellow tail. Restricted to western Indian Ocean.
Length to 15 cm.

Hybrid Angelfish *Apolemichthys xanthurus x trimaculatus*

A natural hybrid where the two parent species occur together and was known as *A. armitagei*. It varies in colour, looking more or less as one of the parent species. It is usually seen solitary in depths of about 20-30 m and moderately common in the Maldives. Most specimens seen by the author were about 20 cm long.

Blue-face Angelfish
Pomacanthus xanthometopon

A large beautiful fish that is easily approached in the Maldives. Normally seen singly along reefs with caves in shallows as well as along deep walls. Adults recognised by their obvious colours. Juveniles and rarely seen. It is similar to other juveniles in genus, but vertical lines almost straight. Widespread Indo-Pacific.
Length to 36 cm.

Emperor Angelfish *Pomacanthus imperator*

Also known as Imperial Angelfish. Common in the Maldives, adults as well as juveniles are normally seen solitary. Various depths but juveniles usually often deep, in caves or large sponges. Feed on various invertebrates, including sponges, and juveniles commonly pick parasites from other fishes in cleaning stations with shrimps. Juveniles identified by circling patterns. Widespread Indo-Pacific, but west Pacific fish develop trailing filament on dorsal fin. Length to 38 cm.

Half-circled Angelfish *Pomacanthus semicirculatus*

Rare in the Maldives. Post-larvae usually settle in very shallow depth on rocky reef with good algae growth, a habitat lacking in the Maldives and probably the cause of its rarity. Adults prefer outer reef walls and are often seen on shipwrecks in depths over 30 m. Juveniles identified by their semi-circle vertical lines over the body. Widespread Indo-Pacific. Length to 35 cm. Photo left, adult: Derawan; juvenile: Flores, Indonesia.

Blue-ringed Angelfish
Pomacanthus annularis

Included here on the basis of a sight record by Herwarth Voigtmann. The adult was seen in deep water. This species is common in mainland waters and often found on silty reefs. Juveniles in very shallow depths, often on jetty pylons. Easily identified by colour pattern. Photos: Bali, Indonesia. Length to 45 cm.

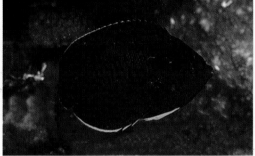

Many-spined Angelfish *Centropyge multispinis*

Occurs in silty and shallow lagoons on coral bommies as well as deep along outer reef walls. Often swims in small groups when feeding on algae. A dark looking species showing little colour other than electric blue margins on the fins. The most common small angel species in the Maldives. Widespread and common in Indian Ocean. Length to 14 cm seen in lagoons, but usually about 10 cm.

Moonbeam Angelfish *Centropyge flavipectoralis*

In the Maldives this species was observed between 20 and 40 metres on mixed rubble-sand reef with sparse sponge and soft coral growth. Adults singly or in small groups. Easily overlooked because of its similarity to the previous common species. It is very similar to the Many-spined Angelfish and best recognised by the yellow pectoral fins on the sides. Indian Ocean.
Length to 10 cm. Photo, right: Singapore Aquarium.

Coral Beauty
Centropyge bispinosa

Rare in the Maldives. Occasionally collected by aquarists. Elsewhere it lives in a great depth range from shallow rich coral lagoons to deep drop-offs to at least 60 m depth. It varies in colour, often more orange in deep water and more blue in shallows. Generally looks blue in natural light. Widespread Indo-Pacific.
Length to 10 cm. Aquarium photo.

Eibl's Angelfish *Centropyge eibli*

Rare in the Maldives. Occasionally collected by aquarists. Shallow reefs with soft coral and hydroid growth to depth of about 25 m. Variable, mainly light grey with thin vertical lines and dusky to black tail. Sometimes orange markings on the head or below lines and in anal fin. Indian Ocean only, ranging east to Bali. Replaced by similar *C. vroliki* in the Pacific. The two species occur together in some areas and commonly produce hybrids. Length to 10 cm. Photo, adult: Java, Indonesia; juvenile: Bali, Indonesia.

Indian Cherup Angelfish
Centropyge acanthops

Rare in the Maldives. Sought after and occasionally collected by aquarists in the south. Coral rich reefs where feeding on algae along the basis. Readily identified by the bright orange head and back and blue below. Reported from depths between 10 and 40 m. Restricted to western Indian Ocean. Length to 8 cm. Photo: taken in Mustag Hussain's aquarium.

Damsel Angelfish
Centropyge flavicauda

Rare in the Maldives, but easily overlooked and usually mistaken for a white-tailed damselfish. Found on rubble zones on the basis of reefs, usually in 10-20 m depth but reported to 60 m. Feeds primarily on algae and settling invertebrate growth on rubble pieces or coral bases. Young dark brown to black, adults with bluish sheen and tail usually whitish. Widespread Indo-Pacific. Length to 8 cm. Photo: Bali, Indonesia.

Lyre-tail Angelfish *Genicanthus caudovittatus*

Deep outer reef walls, usually in 40+ m depth. Rich invertebrate habitat, in caves or ridges at bases of drop-offs. Feeds on zooplankton, as well as benthic invertebrates. Occurs in small loose groups of females and a single male. Males have a barred body-pattern. West Indian Ocean and Red Sea.
Length to 20 cm. Photos: Jörg Aebi.

BATFISHES - EPHIPPIDAE

Small family with 5 genera and about 10 species, of which the genus *Platax* and 3 species occur in the Maldives. Juveniles are extremely tall finned, gradually changing with growth to an almost round profiled fish. Small juveniles are pelagic, floating with land debris such as leaves near the surface or sargassum weeds during the wet season. They form small groups and often settle in harbours under jetties. Adults can be solitary or in groups, preferring deep water but enter shallow water to feed. Diet comprises bottom invertebrates and zooplankton, sometimes seen nibbling jellies.

Rounded Batfish
Platax orbicularis

Also known as Circular Batfish. Adults solitary or in small groups, sometimes schooling. Juveniles nearly always in small groups, swimming close to the bottom in very shallow protected waters after settling from pelagic stage. Pelagic juveniles mimic browned tree leaves. Juveniles are best recognised by two dark spots opposite each other on the tail at the end of the body fins. The adult has yellowish pectoral fins on the sides. Widespread Indo-Pacific.
Length to 50 cm. Photo, juveniles: Indonesia.

Tall-fin Batfish *Platax teira*

Also known as Longfin Batfish. Adults solitary or in small groups. Tiny juveniles float below surface debris, forming groups when finding each other. Often settle under jetties, swimming mid water. Best recognised by black blotch below the pectoral fins on the sides that is part of the broad dark band but usually stands out, and a short dark bar on the anus that may fade in adults but usually visible. Widespread Indo-Pacific. Length to 60 cm.
Photo, adult: Japan; juvenile: Flores, Indonesia. Photo, left: Jörg Aebi.

Boer's Batfish *Platax boersi*

Only recently recognised as being valid and previously confused with other species. Semi-adult was observed at Magelli at close range by the author. Adult very similar to Rounded Batfish. Juveniles similar to Tall-fin Batfish. Adult Boer's batfish have a very short mouth and appear to be 'flat'-faced, whilst juveniles are identified by the tall but somewhat triangularly vertical fins. It appears to be widespread Indo-Pacific. Length to at least 50 cm.
Photos of juveniles and semi-adult: Sulawesi, Indonesia; adult: Jörg Aebi.

HAWKFISHES - CIRRHITIDAE

Moderately large family with 9 genera and 35 species, mainly Indo-Pacific (only 3 known from the Atlantic), of which 6 genera and 8 species are known from the Maldives. Hawkfishes vary in shape from compressed and high bodies to stocky or elongated fish and are best recognised by the little filamentous tufts attached to the tip of each spine in the dorsal fin. They are carnivores that perch themselves on corals to watch out for small prey such as shrimps or juvenile fishes. The various species live on reef crests, surge zones, deep current-channels or in black corals. Some are territorial, others form small groups.

Longnose Hawkfish
Oxycirrhites typus

Usually seen singly in Black Coral bushes, but often occur in pairs. It rests on sponges or large fan corals, and feeds on small creatures and plankton floating past. Easily recognised by the elongated snout and colouration. Moderately common between 15 and 35 m in the Maldives in Black Coral. Widespread Indo-Pacific.
Length to 10 cm.
Photo, side-on: Toshikazu Kozawa.

Spotted Hawkfish
Cirrhitichthys oxycephalus

Very common in the Maldives, almost anywhere on reefs from shallow lagoons to deep along walls, usually resting on top of small coral heads. Variable from purple-brown to bright red with depth. Identified by the uniformly blotched pattern and small spots in the tail fin. Widespread Indo-Pacific.
Length to 9 cm.

Coral Hawkfish
Cirrhitichthys falco

Uncommon in the Maldives, but common in most other parts of the Indo-Pacific where they occur in clear water reefs on crests and slopes to 45 m depth. Identified by the mostly red spots on an almost white body and large spots in the tail fin. Length to 65 mm.
Photo: Mustag Hussain.

Blotched Hawkfish *Cirrhitichthys aprinus*

Rare in the Maldives, primarily a mainland species of coastal waters and harbours. Sometimes in deep water with sponges. Could be mistaken for the Spotted Hawkfish that has similar but smaller spotted body pattern, but addition spots on the tail, that is plain in the Blotched Hawkfish. Widespread tropical Indo-Pacific. Length to 12 cm, usually to 9 cm.
Photo: Jörg Aebi.

Two-spot Hawkfish *Amblycirrhites bimaculata*

Uncommon but secretive species that could easily be overlooked. Typically lives inside reefs in holes that are dark or shaded. Usually shallow surge zones to about 15 m depth. Has a blotched pattern but lacks spots in the fins. A dark eye-size spot on the gill behind the eye and a second one below the soft dorsal fin. Widespread Indo-Pacific.
Length to 75 mm. Photo: Jörg Aebi.

Lyre-tail Hawkfish *Cyprinocirrhites polyactis*

Uncommon in the Maldives. Lives in current prone channels and rises above the bottom to feed on plankton and unlike other hawkfish, it has a lyre-tail that serves better for swimming in currents. It is sometimes mistaken for a basslet that feeds that way. Usually rests on sponges or coralline algae bommies in depths from 10 to 50 m. Length to 65 mm, excluding filaments on tail.
Photo, juvenile and swimming: Bali, Indonesia.
Photo, above right: Jörg Aebi.

Ring-eye Hawkfish *Paracirrhites arcatus*

Also called Horseshoe Hawkfish. Adults singly, sometimes in pairs, in small coral heads on exposed. upper reef slopes Recognised by elliptical ring extending from behind eye. Main body colour from light green to bright red. Widespread Indo-Pacific.
Length to 14 cm.
Photo: Mustag Hussain.

Forster's Hawkfish
Paracirrhites forsteri

Also known as Freckled Hawkfish. A common but variable species in the Maldives with several colour forms. Best identified by the numerous dark spots on the head. Reef crests and slopes, usually shallow to about 20 m depth, but may venture deep. Widespread Indo-Pacific. Length to 20 cm.
Photo, dark form, jawning: Toshikazu Kozawa.
Photo, red juvenile: Bali, Indonesia.

White-spotted Hawkfish
Cirrhitus pinnulatus

Also known as Stocky Hawkfish with a much lower and less compressed body. Probably common in the Maldives, but typically lives in very shallow (to 6 m) surge zones where it clings to the reef in the currents where few divers or snorkelers go unless conditions allow. Feeds on various small creatures. Has a blenny-like appearance and best recognised by the series of white blotches that may appear yellow under water. Widespread Indo-Pacific.
Length to 25 cm.
Photo top: Toshikazu Kozawa.
Photo, bottom: Jörg Aebi.

DAMSELFISHES - POMACENTRIDAE

Very large family with an estimated 30 genera and 300 species globally, mostly tropical but some found in sub-tropical to warm-temperate seas. They are well represented in the Maldives with about 50 species presently known, and more to be expected. They are dividable into several groups and treated here as such.

ANEMONEFISHES - POMACENTRIDAE-1

Anemonefishes are specialised damselfishes that have adapted to living in a symbiotic relationship with anemones, and to such extent that they are rarely seen away from their host. There are about 30 species, all except one in the genus *Amphiprion,* 3 of which known from the Maldives. They can be found through most of the Indo-Pacific and of the 1000 or so anemone species, only 10 play host to these fishes. The greatest diversity of them is found in the New Guinea region. Each fish species has preference for particular anemones but some are more fussy than others, and may live in several species depending on availability and habitat. The anemone doesn't sting the fish as it recognises it as being part of itself. Anemonefishes feed on food drifting past and diet comprises zooplankton but may also nibble on algae growing around coral bases nearby.

Blackfoot Anemonefish
Amphiprion nigripes

The Maldives own anemonefish, not know from anywhere else except nearby Sri Lanka. A common species, easily recognised by the single white bar over the head and the black lower fins. Only known in one host anemone *Heteractis magnifica.* Reef crests and slopes to depths of about 15 m.
Length to 10 cm.
Photo, top: freshly laid eggs on cleared piece of coral rubble, near the foot of anemone.

Yellow-tail Anemonefish
Amphiprion sebae

Usually at moderate depths in the Maldives on sand and rubble flats in clear water to 35 m depth. Recognised by the long all yellow tail. Lives in host anemone *Stichodactyla haddoni*. Widespread in mainland reefs along northern Indian Ocean, ranging to Java, Indonesia. Length to 14 cm.

Clark's Anemonefish *Amphiprion clarkii*

Commonly found in most reef habitats. Highly variable in colour depending on geographical area and host anemone. It is the only species known to live with all host anemones. Maldives fishes are typically coloured as shown in the photographs. Is widespread Indo-Pacific. Length to 14 cm.

HUMBUGS - POMACENTRIDAE-2

All belong in a small genus with 9 species, 3 of which found in the Maldives. Stocky small species, many of which broadly banded, hence the name Humbug. Often occurs in schools amongst corals and some juveniles live in or near tentacles of anemones and amongst long spines of urchins.

Humbug Damsel *Dascyllus aruanus*

A common species in lagoons amongst various branching corals, adults often staghorn corals and juveniles in *Acropora* coral heads that provides more shelter for small fish. Feeds in loose schools above the corals on zooplankton during currents. Easily identified by the black and white banding. The similar *D. melanurus* that has a black tail is not known from the Maldives. Widespread Indo-Pacific. Length to 8 cm.

Indian Humbug *Dascyllus carneus*

Forms small schools around branching *Acropora* coral heads on sheltered reefs, from a few metres depth to almost 30 m. Feed on zooplankton above the corals, quickly diving amongst the coral branches with any sign of danger. Identified by almost white body and single dark band over head. Widespread Indian Ocean, east to Java, Indonesia, replaced by sibling *D. reticulatus* in Pacific.
Length to 6 cm.

Three-spot Humbug *Dascyllus trimaculatus*

Common in most reef habitats, mainly on shallow reef crests and slopes with tall coral growth to 20 m depth, and juveniles often grouping together in large anemones. Juveniles with three large white spots that may disappear in large adults. Readily identified by the black colour. Widespread Indo-Pacific.
Length to 12 cm.

PULLERS - POMACENTRIDAE-3

A single large genus *Chromis* with over 80 species, many of which were recently discovered, and at least 13 species occur in the Maldives. Most are schooling species that live on shallow reef crest, slopes and walls where current carry zooplankton, either from oceanic or lagoon origins. Some live in very deep water only.

Green Puller *Chromis viridis*

Usually occurs in large schools where lagoon currents run across reefs, in particular on crests that have very large colonies of dense branching corals that can accommodate numerous individuals. Mainly inner reefs to about 10 m depth. Plain light green, males turn golden-yellow when nesting. Widespread and common throughout Indo-Pacific. Length to 8 cm.

Blue-green Puller *Chromis atripectoralis*

Often overlooked because of its similarity to the Green Puller and is much less common in the Maldives. It is best distinguished by the black spot at the base of the pectoral fins. Inshore on reef slopes, usually in loose groups to depths of about 20 m. Widespread Indo-Pacific. Length to 10 cm.

Swallow-tail Puller *Chromis ternatensis*

One of the most common pullers in the Maldives, often forming large schools that fill the water column above reefs when feeding on zooplankton. Occurs in most reef habitats with branching corals that are exposed to currents, to about 25 m depth. Plain body, yellowish in the Maldives, and strong black margins along outer rays. Widespread Indo-Pacific, some colour variations. Length to 10 cm.

Buff Puller *Chromis xutha*

Seen singly or small loose groups along drop-offs in or near caves. Feeds on zooplankton close to the reefs, mainly lives in clear water habitats to about 30 m depth. Plain light brown and long filaments on tail when adult. Only known from the western Indian Ocean. Length to 75 mm.

Pemba Puller *Chromis pembae*

Outer reef habitat, usually in depths between 20 and 50 m. Seen singly or in small scattered groups. Feeds on zooplankton. Variable dark brown to yellow. Identified by yellow marginal band in spinous dorsal fin and white ventral fins. West Indian Ocean and Red Sea. Length to 75 mm.
Photo: Jörg Aebi.

Two-tone Puller *Chromis dimidiata*

Clear water habitat from 5 to 30 m depth, usually at about 10 m in small caves or crevices. Usually seen singly in reefs, staying close to the bottom. Easily recognised by partly black body and white tail colouration. Widespread Indian Ocean, ranging to southern Java, Indonesia.
Length to 7 cm.

White-finned Puller *Chromis flavipectoralis*

Occurs in clear lagoons and inner reefs on reef slopes and walls with rich coral growth. Usually seen solitary and adults in moderate depths along walls in 20+ m. Juveniles shallow in rich coral areas. Identified by the white ventral fins. Only known from Maldives to Java, Indonesia, reported from shallow depths, outside Maldives.
Length to 8 cm.

Deep-reef Puller *Chromis delta*

Found in clear water reefs, mainly in caves along inner and outer reef walls from 15 to 40 m depth, reported to 80 m. Occurs in small loose groups, staying close to the bottom and common where found. Identified by dark grey body, abruptly changing to white at the tail base, and long double filaments at tips of fin. Widespread Indo-Pacific.
Length to 7 cm.

Twin-spot Puller *Chromis elerae*

Moderately common on steep reef walls, coastal to outer reefs where large caves with rich invertebrate growth available. Often swims upside down near ceilings of large overhangs in small loose groups, usually deep from 20 m down. Identified by generally dark grey colour and the pale twin spots on the tail base. Widespread Indo-Pacific.
Length to 65 mm.

Scaly Puller *Chromis lepidolepis*

A rarely noticed species because of lack of colour or distinctive pattern. Inhabits reef crests and slopes on inner and outer reefs, usually solitary or in small loose groups, to about 20 m depth. Mainly light greenish grey, only distinguishing feature is vertical black bar in eye. Widespread Indo-Pacific.
Length to 8 cm.

Double-bar Puller *Chromis opercularis*

Inshore to outer reef crests, various depths but inshore usually in depths of about 10 m and on outer reefs shallower. Prefers current prone reefs and feeds hight above the bottom on zooplankton, ranging to 40 m depth. Widespread Indo-Pacific, but numerous geographical variations that often look like totally different species. Photograph shows typical Maldives fish.
Length to 12 cm.

Weber's Puller *Chromis weberi*

Inner reef crests and slopes to depths of about 25 m. Common but a dull species not often noticed. Mainly plain greenish grey, sometimes has yellowish sides. Best identified by the double dark bar on the head and dark tips on the tail fin. Widespread Indo-Pacific.
Length to 10 cm.

Black-fin Puller *Chromis nigroanalis*

Usually found solitary in moderate depths along outer reef walls between 20 and 40 m. Deep-bodied, bluish grey species and named for the large black area on the anal fin. Widespread Indian Ocean, ranging to Java but generally rare.
Length to 11 cm.
Photo: Jörg Aebi.

Black-edged Puller *Chromis nigrura*

A moderately common but small species on reef crests with rich coral growth and often with moderate surge on outer reefs, found down to about 30 m depth. Recognised by the yellow tail and dark blue-black anal fin. Widespread Indian Ocean, mainly oceanic locations, and not yet known from Indonesia.
Length to 55 mm.
Photo: Jörg Aebi.

DAMSELS - POMACENTRIDAE-4

This groups comprises the species generally called damsels. The genus *Pomacentrus* the largest with 53 species distributed throughout the Indo-Pacific, 6 of which found in the Maldives. The genus *Neopomacentrus* with 13 species and only one recorded from the Maldives. The genus *Amblypomacentrus* thought to be containing a single species, but a seemingly new one found in the Maldives. The genus *Chrysiptera* with 25 species, 4 of which found in the Maldives. Most of these species associate with coral reefs and stay close to the bottom.

Blue-yellow Damsel *Pomacentrus caeruleus*

Common in the Maldives and readily noticed by the bright blue colour of the body and yellow lower fins and tail. Occurs in small groups on shallow clear water reef crests with mixed rubble and good coral growth. Appears to be restricted to western Indian Ocean, replaced by similar species in east Indian and Pacific Oceans. Length to 8 cm.

Azure Damsel *Pomacentrus pavo*

Coastal, often silty reefs, particularly common on large remote bommies on sand in deep lagoons. Forms small to large aggregations in those areas, commonly darting in and out of holes. Colour highly variable from pale green to bright blue, often an earspot shows dark or reflective green. Widespread and generally common in coastal habitats throughout the Indo-Pacific.
Length to 10 cm.

Scribbled Damsel *Pomacentrus nagasakiensis*

Moderately common in the Maldives and seems to have been overlooked until now. The photographs represent the first records for the Maldives and Indian Ocean. Generally deep on sand flats over 20 m, but commonly found around remote coral heads in those habitats. Was only known from the West Pacific between Japan and Australia but now seems widespread. Length to 10 cm.

Indian Damsel *Pomacentrus indicus*

Common in the Maldives and usually juveniles are noted because of the bright orange over the top. This gradually reduces with size and adults are dull coloured. Found from shallow inshore to outer reef habitats, adults ranging to deep water to 40 m depth. Distributed throughout central Indian Ocean. Length to 11 cm.

Philippine Damsel *Pomacentrus philippinus*

Moderately common in clear inner and outer reef channels and along drop-offs with caves and overhangs, usually in depths between 10 and 40 m. Mostly seen solitary, and easily recognised by the bright yellow tail, the typical form in the Maldives. Widespread west Pacific, and ranging west to the Maldives. Length to 10 cm.

White-tail Damsel *Pomacentrus chrysurus*

Shallow reef crests and slopes, in the Maldives usually on outer reef flats with moderate surge in 6 to 15 m depth. Juveniles orange over the head and part of body and the white tail that is prominent when adult is not always evident. Widespread west Pacific, ranging west to the Maldives. Length to 9 cm.

Regal Damsel *Neopomacentrus cyanomos*

A common continental species that usually occurs in coastal reef habitats. Mainly grey with a distinctive small white spot at end of dorsal fin base. Spot less obvious in large individuals that develop long angular to filamentous lobes at the ends of the dorsal, anal and tail fins. Widespread Indo-Pacific, some geographical variations.
Length to 10 cm. Photo: Java, Indonesia.

Lyretail damsel *Amblypomacentrus* sp 1

Photographed in a silty lagoon at about 35 m depth where this species was common. Typically for the genus on open bottom with rubbish lying around that is used for refuge and nesting. A new discovery for the Maldives, and represents only the second species for the genus that was thought to be restricted to the west Pacific.
Length to 10 cm, including filamentous parts on tail.

White-saddled Damsel *Chrysiptera biocellata*

A common species in the Maldives found on shallow inshore waters, still lagoons and harbours, often silty reefs with lots of coral rubble, and in seagrass areas with rubble patches. Rarely deeper than 5 m. Identified by the white bar slightly forward from centre of body. Widespread Indo-Pacific, but some geographical variations. Length to 11 cm.

Surge Damsel *Chrysiptera brownriggii*

Common, and as the name suggests: on surge reefs. Found mainly on outer reef flats with channels and good algae growth, less common where coral becomes prolific. Two distinctive colour forms that look like two different species, probably sex related. One dull and banded, the other with a bright blue band along the top. Widespread Indian Ocean. Replaced by similar *C. leucopoma* in West Pacific. Length to 8 cm. Photo, orange form: Java, Indonesia.

One-spot Damsel *Chrysiptera unimaculata*

Shallow inshore reefs and harbours. A territorial species that occurs in large numbers spread out over the preferred habitat such as dead coral pieces used along break waters in harbours. In the Maldives recognised by the yellow pectoral fins. Widespread Indo-Pacific, but one of the most variable damsels with numerous geographical forms to such extent that it seems like several different species are involved. Length to 85 mm.

Pale-blue Damsel *Chrysiptera glauca*

Mainly found in intertidal zones and often silty habitat. Patchy occurrence in the Maldives but common where found. Rarely deeper than a few metres. Adults identified by plain blue-grey colour. Juveniles brighter blue and a thin iridescent blue line along upper sides from behind the eye to below dorsal fin. Widespread Indo-Pacific.
Length to 10 cm.
Photo: Flores, Indonesia.

Fusilier Damsel *Lepidozygus tapeinosoma*

The single species in this genus is commonly found in the Maldives in lagoons and inner reefs. Usually occurs in small to large schools around coral heads and feeds high above the bottom on zooplankton. Slender species with metallic green body but changes colour when feeding or when in reefs, usually darkening when going into holes. Males, guarding eggs show a broad white band. Widespread Indo-Pacific.
Length to 10 cm.
Photo, individual with cleaner wrasse: Jörg Aebi.

A group of deep bodied damsels that usually have a broadly banded pattern or several stripes, such as is used in the armed forces to show ranks with shoulder pads, like Sergeant, hence the name. Some species occur abundantly in their favourite habitat but others prefer small groups. Mainly inshore, the genus *Abudefduf* comprises 18 species, 5 of which recorded from the Maldives and is represented in the Atlantic with one species. The genus *Amblyglyphidodon* comprises 7 species and two are known from the Maldives.

Sergeant Major *Abudefduf vaigiensis*

Very common in the Maldives and found from inshore to inner reefs, often forming large schools in various depths to about 20 m. Community spawner, eggs deposited on flat surfaces and guarded by the parents, usually timed in phase with full moon. Easily recognised by colour pattern as shown in photograph. Widespread Indo-Pacific, small juveniles often under floating sargassum weeds and distributed over great distances.
Length to 15 cm.

Yellow-tail Sergeant *Abudefduf notatus*

Coastal reefs and often in freshwater run offs. Schools and often seen swimming along reef slopes well away from reefs. Deposits eggs inside caves rather than open surfaces compared to other sergeants. Easily identified by the yellow tail. Widespread Indo-Pacific, Length to 20 cm.

Nine-band Sergeant *Abudefduf septemfasciatus*

A very shallow water species found in sheltered bays with large boulders, rock or concrete structures such as used in harbours for break waters. Juveniles intertidal and in rockpools. Upper parts of the bands often extra dark, distinguishing it from other similar species. Widespread Indo-Pacific.
Length to 20 cm. Photo, nuptial male with darkened colours: Neville Coleman.

Black-spot Sergeant
Abudefduf sordidus

Inshore reefs, rubble and boulder slopes and often around jetties in harbours. Small juveniles often stranded in pools on low tides. Bands broad and pale inter-spaces much narrower. A black spot on top of tail base usually obvious. Widespread Indo-Pacific.
Length to 20 cm.
Photo: Bali, Indonesia.

Scissortail Sergeant
Abudefduf sexfasciatus

Doubtfully reported from the Maldives, possible an expatriate in northern atolls or south of the equator where currents run opposite ways. Usually common where found. Reef crests on inshore reefs with rich soft coral growth. Widespread Indo-Pacific, and commonly found along continental waters of the Indian Ocean.
Length to 15 cm.
Photo: Bali, Indonesia.

White-breasted Sergeant
Amblyglyphidodon leucogaster

Inshore to outer reef habitats, usually seen solitary in areas with rich coral growth. Reported to 45 m depth. Widespread Indo-Pacific, but several geographical variations. In the Maldives mainly greenish and a dark bar on the cheek.
Length to 12 cm.

Green Sergeant
Amblyglyphidodon batunai

A recently described species from Indonesia. Commonly found in sandy lagoons with staghorn coral patches to about 10 m depth, usually in small groups swimming above the corals to feed on zooplankton. Plain greenish colour, lacking any distinctive features.
Length to 15 cm.

This group of damsels associate to algae habitats to various degrees. Some feeding on algae as part of their diet and others to such extent that they promote the growth of algae by giving nature a helping hand: devoting most of the time to clear areas and keeping invaders at bay. Genus *Plectroglyphidodon* comprises 9 species restricted to Indo-Pacific, 5 of which found in the Maldives and *Stegastes* has over 30 species globally, 4 of which known from the Maldives.

Jewel Damsel
Plectroglyphidodon lacrymatus

Found in various reef habitats with good algae growth, including exposed outer reef slopes where algae is dominant in the shallows. Aggressive and territorial. Easily recognised by the bright blue spots when juvenile, or the bright eyes when adult. Common in the Maldives. Widespread Indo-Pacific. Length to 10 cm.

Narrowbar Damsel *Plectroglyphidodon dickii*

Coral reef crests with mixed rich coral and algae growth around the coral bases. Often in surge zones on outer reefs in shallow depths, ranging to about 10 m depth. Sometimes in small loose groups sharing large coral formations. Readily identified by the black bar near the tail followed by white in juveniles and yellow in large adults. Widespread Indo-Pacific. Length to 10 cm.

Johnston's Damsel
Plectroglyphidodon johnstonianus

Clear water reefs, usually restricted to outer reef slopes but only known from a few sightings in the Maldives. Shallow reef crests with rich coral growth, rarely deeper than 10 m. Similar to Narrowbar Damsel but black bar wider and not defined at edges, sometimes absent, generally more yellow, and some blue on head and in eyes. Widespread Indo-Pacific. Length to 9 cm. Photo: Charles Anderson.

White-band Damsel
Plectroglyphidodon leucozonus

Typically found in shallow high energy zones and not often observed by divers unless conditions allow, rarely deeper than 5 m. Mainly brown with a pale band across the body, band broad and distinctive in juveniles, narrowing with age and sometimes barely visible. Widespread Indo-Pacific.
Length to 16 cm. Photo: Sulawesi, Indonesia.

Sharp-eye Damsel
Plectroglyphidodon imparipennis

Clear outer reefs on shallow surge slopes, usually in depths less than 3 m. Variable in colour with plain to bright yellow tail. Eye white with short vertical black bar. Widespread Indo-Pacific with several geographical variations. Small species, length to 60 mm.
Photo: Jerry Allen, Christmas Island, Indian Ocean.

White-banded Gregory
Stegastes albifasciatus

Uncommon in the Maldives. Found in high surge zones on outer reef slopes in the northernmost atolls. Usually in a few metres depth. Usually all dark, sometimes a broad pale band, a blue spot on each scale in the dark area, and a distinctive black spot with white in front at end of dorsal fin base. Widespread Indo-Pacific, but highly variable with several geographical colour forms that seem like other species.
Length to 15 cm. Photo: Flores, Indonesia.

Indian Gregory *Stegastes cf fasciolatus* sp 1

Undetermined species on algae rich reefs in lagoons and on inner reefs. Thought to be geographical variation, but looks quite different from the Pacific *S. fasciolatus* as juvenile as well as adult. Juveniles with yellow tail and black spot heading dorsal fin. Usually seen solitary. Probably throughout Indian Ocean.
Length to about 10 cm.
Photo, adult: Christmas Island, Indian Ocean, Jerry Allen.

Blunt-snout Gregory
Stegastes lividus

Commonly occurs in lagoons amongst large staghorn coral patches, to 7 m depth. Best recognised by the black tail fin base spot outlined with iridescent blue and light coloured chest. Usually in small loose groups. Aggressive to other fishes and even divers when caring for eggs. Widespread Indo-Pacific.
Length to 16 cm.

✓ (foot Sucker)

Dusky Gregory
Stegastes nigricans

Inshore and often in silty lagoons or harbours. Usually in rocky or dead coral reef habitat, and algae reefs to about 10 m depth. Variable in colour, usually plain with dark spot on top of tail. Widespread Indo-Pacific.
Length to 14 cm.

BARRACUDAS - SPHYRAENIDAE

This primarily tropical family comprises a single genus with about 20 species globally, 6 of which reported from the Maldives but several possible errors, eg *Sphyraena novaehollandiae* is a temperate Australian species. Predatory fishes, recently reclassified and placed closely to species such as tunas. Some species school in open water and are occasionally seen near reef such as the Black Tail Barracuda *S. genie*. some species only visit reefs at night. The most commonly observed is the Great Barracuda, included here.

Great Barracuda *Sphyraena barracuda*

Usually seen solitary, swimming along deep slopes, occasionally entering shallow depths. Usually in depths over 10 m, and occasionally in small groups. Juveniles in sheltered inshore habitats, including mangroves. Widespread in all tropical seas, in some regions forming large schools. Reported to 100 m depth.
Length to 1.9 m. Photo: Neville Coleman.

MULLETS - MUGILIDAE

A large family with about 15 genera and over 70 species globally, 3 of which recorded from the Maldives. Coastal, inshore fishes in estuaries, harbours and often entering freshwater. Schools are frequently seen on the surface close to shore over shallow sand flats, occasionally dipping down to feed on the sand surface.

Warty-lip Mullet
Crenimugil crenilabis

A schooling species, probably most observed species by divers, in sheltered bays. Swims at various depths along reefs to about 20 m depth, feeds by scooping the upper layer of sand or mud to filter various food items, including tiny animals and algae. Widespread Indo-Pacific.
Large species, length to 40 cm. Also in the Maldives: the very similar Bluespot Mullet *Moolgarda seheli* has a deeper forked tail fin and is more estuarine.

Fringe-lip Mullet
Oedalechilus labiosus

Occurs in small groups, commonly in harbours and protected bays in the Maldives, often silty conditions. Swims near the surface around jetties and rocks. Has a rather blunt pointed snout compared to other Maldives species. Widespread Indo-Pacific.
Length to 25 cm.

WRASSES - LABRIDAE

One of the largest families of reef fishes as presently defined with more than 60 genera and 400+ species worldwide, of which 27 genera and at least 66 species occur in the Maldives. No doubt more will be discovered over time. Many species go through tremendous colour changes with growth and sex. Usually each individual starts adulthood as female, becoming part of a group that is dominated by a male that is normally the largest individual. The most dominant female is next in line and changes sex to reign. Sizes range from a few centimetres to several metres as adults. Although all species are diurnal, the various groups either sleep under sand, in crevices or simply lay on the bottom. As there are a number of distinctively different groups, based on both looks and behaviour, each is treated here separately with an introduction write-up to be able to simplify basic information.

SAND WRASSES - LABRIDAE-1

A large number of wrasses associate with sand where they bury to escape danger, or to sleep. The various species occupy different habitats that range from open sand flats to small patches surrounded by reefs. The wrasses adapted to live on open sand falts are known as razor fishes or knife fishes. They are strongly compressed, thin and have a sharp keel-like forehead that enable them to bury in the sand fast, and with ease. Some can swim for a long distance through the sand by vibrating the body. Normally these fishes have a special patch of sand prepared to bury, sometimes several, where the coarse and sharp bits have been removed. Small juveniles are often brightly coloured and look completely different from the adults. Those on sand may be yellow or green, even white phases, and those visiting reefs are red or have distinctive patterns if lines and spots. Males can also differ considerably from females. The genus *Coris* has about 25 species, 3 of which known from the Maldives; *Hologymnosus* has 4 species, 2 of which known from the Maldives; *Cheilio* has a single species; *Cymolutes* has 3, one of which in the Maldives; *Novaculichthys* has about 7 species, some undescribed, one in the Maldives; *Xyrichtys* has about 25 species, 2 in the Maldives; *Pseudocoris* has 5 species, one of which in the Maldives; and *Pseudojuloides* has 9 species, one of which in the Maldives.

Variegated Wrasse
Coris batuensis

A common lagoon species, also on sheltered sandy reefs, usually in small loose groups. Juveniles on algae and rubble patches or seagrass patches and found to about 30 m depth. Little change with growth or between sexes. Widespread Indo-Pacific, some geographical variations. Closely related *C. variegata* is Red Sea only.
Length to 20 cm.
Photo above: Toshikazu Kozawa.

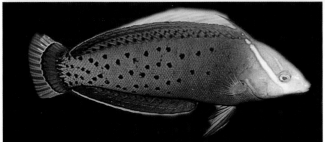

Queen Wrasse
Coris frerei

Occurs at moderate depths, adults at about 30 m, often sand channels between reefs with rubble on the bottom. Juveniles shallow on sand patches. The large male solitary and has a large territory, defended against neighbouring males. They feed on various small creatures that are often caught by turning over pieces of rubble, lifting with their snout. West Indian Ocean, moderately common in the Maldives. Length to 50 cm.
Photo: juvenile, right : Jörg Aebi.

African Wrasse *Coris cuvieri*
Adults in small loose groups, usually a large male in the area, on shallow reefs with sand channels or rubble patches. Small juveniles on exposed reefs close to surge zone. Adults to about 20 m depth, occasionally venturing deep. Indian Ocean species, common in the Maldives ranging to northern Java, overlapping in range with the Pacific sibling *C. gaimard*. Previously called *C. africana*.
Length to 35 cm.
Photo, above: juvenile: Jörg Aebi.

Ringed Wrasse *Hologymnosus annulatus* ✓

Shallow reef crests and slopes to about 25 m depth, usually over sand and rubble areas. Small juveniles often in small groups, adults seen solitary with male patrolling very large territory. Photographing a male can be very difficult. It's best to wait when finding a female, as eventually the male will come to check her out. Several changes with growth. Large males green, sometimes showing pale band during display. Juveniles with black over most of the lower half fo body and head. Widespread Indo-Pacific.
Length to 40 cm. Photo, male: Bali, Indonesia.

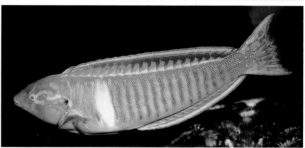

Narrow-banded Wrasse *Hologymnosus doliatus*

Clear outer reef habitat, deep sand flats on rubble zones below drop-offs and slopes or near large bommies. Rare in the Maldives. Several were seen and photographed along a reef edge on sand about 12 cm long, represents first record. Small juveniles have horizontal lines and gradually changes to a barred pattern of the adult. More elongate than most wrasses. Widespread Indo-Pacific. Length to 30 cm. Photo, male: Bali, Indonesia.

Cigar Wrasse
Cheilio inermis

Intertidal to about 20 m depth. Not often observed by divers, but lives mainly in seagrass areas that are suffering from development of resorts, making the species rare in those areas. Very elongate and usually greenish grey. Sometimes has yellow phase in soft corals, but this form rare in the Maldives. Widespread Indo-Pacific.
Length to 48 cm.
Photographs: Indonesia.

Knife Wrasse *Cymolutes praetextatus*

Occurs in small loose groups on shallow sand flats and near seagrass beds. Common in the Maldives. Usually in depths less than 10 m. Indo-Pacific. Variable in colour to suit habitat, usually a tiny dark spot like a speck of dirt on upper part of the tail base. Reported length to 20 cm probably based on other species in genus, largest ever seen by author is about 10 cm.

Reindeer Wrasse
Novaculichthys taeniourus

Also called Rockmover Wrasse. Adults nearly always in pairs, juveniles solitary. Typically found on rubble reef and sand flats with rubble ridges from shallow surge zones to deep water, observed to 45 m depth. Lifts and turns large rubble pieces to catch small creatures from underneath such as crabs. When in pairs, usually one lifts and the other catches, taking turns. Widespread Indo-Pacific. Length to 25 cm.
Photo, large juvenile: Jörg Aebi; baby: Toshikazu Kozawa.

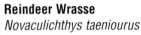

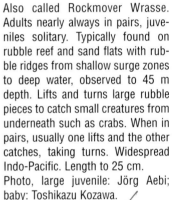

White-blotch Razorfish
Xyrichtys aneitensis

A common species on sand flats, slopes and ridges, often in spread out groups, each with its own sand patch prepared to bury. Quickly dives in the sand when approached. Shallow to at least 40 m depth. Small juveniles highly variable in colour from white, green, brown or black becoming sandy coloured with vertical bars. Adults with large white blotch on sides. Widespread Indo-Pacific.
Length to 20 cm.

Blue Razorfish
Xyrichtys pavo

Adults usually on deep sand slopes, in excess of 50 m. Several individuals observed by the author in the Maldives depths between 15 and 40 m. This species is easily overlooked because of habitat and shyness. Small juveniles with greatly extended first dorsal fin spines like a stem of a leaf. First two spines separate from the rest, connected by a membrane only when small. Juveniles variable from green to brown, developing false eyes in dorsal fin. Males plain blue with a small distinctive spot on sides. Widespread Indo-Pacific.
Length to 30 cm. Photo, male: Sulawesi, Indonesia.

Pink Wrasse *Pseudocoris yamashiroi*

adults occurs in small groups over deep sand flats near reefs or around bommies. Swims high above the bottom to feed on zooplankton. Small juveniles also form small groups but stay close together near the reefs or bommies. Seen in the Maldives to 35 m depth. Small juveniles bright pink, becoming paler with age. Widespread Indo-Pacific. Length to 16 cm, but about 12 cm in the Maldives. Photo, female: Jörg Aebi.

Blue-nose Wrasse *Pseudojuloides kaleidos*

Uncommon and lives on rubble reef slopes and flats in 20 to 35 m depth. This species was first discovered in Male Atoll but now known from Indonesia as well. Females brownish pink, juvenile with pale yellow snout-tip. Males change from female colouration within a week to gaudy colours. Indo-Pacific, known distribution sporadic, probably widespread. Length to 10 cm. Photo, male: John E. Randall; females: Java, Indonesia.

This group of wrasses are mainly found on reefs but burrow in the sand to sleep. Some of the members within this group could be included in the previous group as they are mainly sand-dwellers, but belong in a large genus of which most other members are typical reef dwellers. All the species form loose groups of females, dominated by a single male that has a section of reef as territory. Nearly all feed on the bottom on small invertebrates, only *Leptojulis* is a plankton feeder, some including algae in their diet. None of the species grow large, about 10 to 20 cm long. They are quick, relying on speed and reef coverage to escape danger, but bury in the sand to sleep. Juveniles and females are often similar but males are usually very different in colour. At some stage, many male and female forms where known as different species. Genus *Macropharyngodon* has 10 species, 2 of which in the Maldives; *Halichoeres* has about 65 species, 9 of which in the Maldives; *Leptojulis* has 5 species, 1 in the Maldives; *Stethojulis* has 8 species, 3 of which in the Maldives; *Anampses* has 13 species, 4 of which in the Maldives; *Pseudodax* has a single species.

Splendid Leopard Wrasse
Macropharyngodon bipartitus

Clear reef habitat with rich invertebrate growth. Juveniles and females are often feeding together in small groups on rubble reef. Males are so different from the females that they could easily be mistaken for separate species. All phases readily identified by colour. A common but beautiful Maldives species with restricted west Indian Ocean distribution. Also known as Divided or Vermiculate Wrasse. Depth range is 3 to about 30 m. Length to 13 cm.

Ornate Leopard Wrasse *Macropharyngodon ornatus*

Lives on rubble reef in small groups. Ranges in depth from shallow reef-crests to about 30 m. Differences between sexes is not as great as in most other species in the genus. Colour patterns of both sexes are diagnostic. Uncommon in the Maldives. Indo-Pacific, ranging to Flores, Indonesia.
Length to 11 cm Photo, side-on: Bali, Indonesia.

Lemon Meringue Wrasse
Halichoeres leucoxanthus

A common species in the Maldives, often seen in small groups on sand and rubble along reef edges. Usually in depths over 20 m, and often individuals are seen following goatfishes that disturb the sand for an easy feed. Readily identified by the bright yellow backs and white below. Indian Ocean, ranging east to Java, Indonesia.
Length to 12 cm.

Indian White Wrasse
Halichoeres trispilus

This species prefers deep walls where it can be found in small groups. Occurs on sandy rubble patches on the bottom of large overhangs, usually in depths over 20 m. It appears to be white with natural light at the depth it occurs, because water filters out the red. Originally discovered in the Maldives, but ranges east to southern Java, Indonesia, replaced by sibling *H. pallidus* in the Pacific.
Length to 12 cm.

Adorned Wrasse
Halichoeres cosmetus

Common species in the Maldives, often seen on shallow rubble reef patches on flats and slopes to about 20 m depth, occasionally venturing deeper. Usually in small loose groups swimming close to the bottom. Juveniles amongst large rubble. Pale green with pink lines, juveniles and females with double black spot in dorsal fin. West Indian Ocean only, similar to *H. ornatus* from the Pacific.
Length to 12 cm.

Vrolik's Wrasse *Halichoeres vrolikii*

Common species on protected reefs and in lagoons in heavy coral growth areas, less numerous on outer reefs. Occurs in small loose groups to about 20 m depth. Identified by greenish colour, female with numerous lines from snout to tail, males with series of pale blotches or short bars on body at dorsal fin base. Widespread Indian Ocean, replaced by sibling *H. melanurus* in the Pacific. Length to 12 cm.

Dusky Wrasse
Halichoeres marginatus

Moderately common in the Maldives. Adults swim close to reef and can be found in shallow surge areas to deep reefs and shipwrecks. Juveniles secretive in reef. Juveniles almost black with thin longitudinal lines and large blotch in dorsal fin, changing gradually to the green and gold coloured male. Widespread Indo-Pacific. Length to 18 cm, usually 15 cm.

Zigzag Wrasse *Halichoeres scapularis*

This species is common on sand flats on reef edges or in lagoons. Often follows goatfishes or emperors to feed on the creatures that run away when the sand is disturbed. Usually in loose aggregations with a single large colourful male in charge. Very pale in the Maldives, usually a short black line following eye. Great depth range from inter tidal to at least 50 m. Widespread Indo-Pacific. Length to 15 cm. Photo, juvenile: Jörg Aebi.

Clouded Wrasse
Halichoeres nebulosus

Not commonly observed in the Maldives where only seen in shallows. Prefers shallow surge zones with algal reef but also in harbours on rubble. Highly variable in colour from green to brown or pink, depending on habitat, usually a pink patch on the belly. Male has pink band on cheek. A widespread and common continental species of the Indo-Pacific. Found to 40 m depth in some areas. Length to 12 cm.
Photo, male: Bali, Indonesia.

Checkerboard Wrasse
Halichoeres hortulanus

Found in shallow lagoons to reef slopes to about 25 m, occasionally deeper. Adults usually singly, swimming well above reefs. Males have large territory, females are variously distributed over reef. Adults whitish with yellow tail, a single yellow saddle below spinous dorsal fin and a black spot on upper tail fin base. Widespread Indo-Pacific, but some colour differences between Indian Ocean and Pacific, both forms found in Bali.
Length to 25 cm.
Photo, juvenile: Bali, Indonesia.

Sri Lankan Wrasse
Halichoeres zeylonicus

A common species on deep sand flats with rubble patches and remote bommies, often far away from reefs. Swims in loose groups with a male dominating. In the Maldives it seems to prefer depths of 25+ m. Widespread Indian Ocean, replaced by similar *H. hartzfeldi* in Pacific, ranges of the two species overlap in Bali. The species are identified by different cheek patterns.
Length to 15 cm.

Blue-spot Wrasse
Leptojulis cyanopleura

Photograph represents first record for the Maldives, but it lives on deep open sand flats away from reefs around remote coral bommies and easily could be overlooked. Elsewhere it occurs in shallow coastal waters as well as deep. Several small groups were found in different atholls, in depths of about 30 to 40 m. Slender species, females pale with dark mid-lateral stripe, male with a reflective blue spot in the dark band behind pectoral fin. Widespread Indo-Pacific.
Length to 12 cm.
Photo, displaying male: Bali, Indonesia.

Blue-lined Wrasse *Stethojulis albovittata*

Common in most reef habitats, usually in shallow depth and swimming in small but loose aggregations above the reef. Males swim fast mainly using the pectoral fin on their sides. Males identified by the lower line bending upwards over the pectoral fin base, and females with bright yellow cheek. Indian Ocean, east to Java, Indonesia. Replaced by nearly identical *S. bandanensis* in the Pacific.
Length to 14 cm. Photos, dark male and light female: Jörg Aebi.

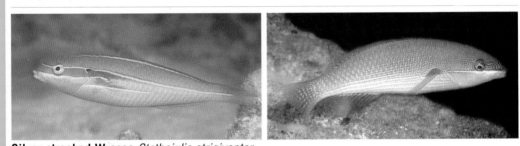

Silver-streaked Wrasse *Stethojulis strigiventer*

Moderately common in lagoons and near seagrass beds, often in silty conditions. Swims in small aggregations, males nearly always on the move. Small juveniles in seagrasses or algaes. Shallow reefs, usually in depths less than 10 m. Slender compared to other members in genus. Female with white streaks along belly. Juveniles green. Widespread Indo-Pacific. Length to 12 cm.

Blue-ribbon Wrasse *Stethojulis trilineata*

Mainly found on outer reef slopes and along upper parts of drop-offs with rich coral growth, including surge zones. Often swimming through gutters or channels and seems less territorial than most wrasses as several males are often seen close together. Shallow to about 15 m depth. Males identified by longer blue lines and two running onto tail fin. Widespread Indo-Pacific. Length to 14 cm. Photo, female: Flores, Indonesia.

Diamond Wrasse *Anampses caeruleopunctatus*

Not common and mainly seen on reef crests adjacent to deep water in the Maldives. Mainly in surge prone areas with mixed algae and coral habitat. Usually small groups of females observed. Large males territorial, often venturing deep, to about 30 m. Females with a bright blue spot on each scale, large males become deep bodies and are mostly blue, showing a pale band over the body just behind the head. Widespread Indo-Pacific. Length to 30 cm. Photo, male: Sulawesi, Indonesia.

White-dashes Wrasse
Anampses lineatus

Deep water habitat, along walls or rich coral-rock shelves in 25+ m depth. Uncommon and seen singly or in small numbers. Could be mistaken for a juvenile Speckled Wrasse (next species) but has white tail and spots on the body are elongated to dashes forming lines in adults. Indian Ocean, ranging to Bali, Indonesia, where its Pacific sibling *A. melanurus* also occurs. Length to 12 cm.

Speckled Wrasse *Anampses meleagrides*

Also called Yellow-tail Wrasse. Females are usually noted for their distinctive colouration, swimming often in small loose groups in coral rich areas. The male is colourful but usually brightens when displaying to the female. Females easily identified by the yellow tail. Mainly shallow reefs to about 20 m depth. Indo-Pacific. Length to 22 cm.

Yellow-Breasted Wrasse *Anampses twistii*

Usually seen solitary in rich coral reefs or along steep walls, swimming close or through the corals, to depth of at least 25 m. Small juveniles have false eyes at the end of dorsal and anal fins, often swimming with head down and the side on view looks more like the face of a larger fish. Large adults recognised by yellow below eye level from mouth to belly. Indo-Pacific. A widespread species, but not particularly common anywhere. Length to 16 cm. Photo, juvenile: Japan.

Chisel-tooth Wrasse
Pseudodax moluccanus

Often seen in caves along deep drop-offs to at least 40 m depth. Small juveniles secretive in crevices and may clean other fishes from parasites. Adults feed on encrusting invertebrates that are uncovered by hacking into their protective cover by strong chisel-like teeth. Juveniles black with two blue horizontal bands. Adults become spotted, usually yellow on the mouth. Widespread Indo-Pacific. Length to 25 cm.

CLEANER WRASSES - LABRIDAE-3

A small group of specialised fishes, especially the genus *Labroides,* that spend much of their lives removing parasites from other fishes. Tiny post-larvae juveniles settle in caves or crevices and their colour pattern combined with dance-like swimming is immediately recognised by other fishes. Adults often work in pairs, using special places on reefs that are known as cleaning stations. Different kinds of fish come in for inspections and removal of itchy parasites. Towards the end of the day it can get very busy with many customers lining up to be serviced. Even some rarely seen pelagic fishes come in at times. Many other wrasse species clean on occasion, or as juvenile only, and vary their diet with coral polyps. Juveniles of the genera *Labrobsis* and *Labrichthys* clean regularly, but adults only part time or not at all. Genus *Labroides* comprises 5 species, 2 of which in the Maldives; *Labrobsis* has 6 species, one in the Maldives; and *Labrichthys* has a single species.

Blue-streak Cleaner Wrasse *Labroides dimidiatus*

Found on shallow lagoon reefs as well as deep on coral bommies to at least 40 m depth. Juveniles solitary and adults usually in pairs. Small juveniles all black with an iridescent blue line, adults become white on the belly and in some populations yellow over the back. Common in the Maldives and the most famous cleaner fish. Widespread Indo-Pacific. Length to 10 cm.

Photo, arguing pair: Java, Indonesia: small juvenile: Toshikazu Kozawa.

Two-colour Cleaner Wrasse
Labroides bicolor

Nearly always seen singly, adults often swimming in the open and cleaning large fishes high above the bottom and covering large sections of reef. Juveniles in caves along walls. Moderately common in the Maldives and has large depth range to at least 50 m. Adults are readily identified by the abruptly changing colour on the body and tail from dark blue to almost white or yellow. Widespread Indo-Pacific. Length to 15 cm.

V-tail Tubelip Wrasse
Labrobsis xanthonota

Lives in rich coral habitat near outer reefs. Mainly shallow in 6 to 25 m depth. Juveniles and females swim in small groups with similar sized individuals, and are dominated by a territorial male. Feeds mainly on coral polyps when adult. Females and juveniles are easily identified by the dark body that is light on top, usually the other way around in fishes, and the male has the unusual 'V' tail. Indo-Pacific. Length to 10 cm.

Tube-mouth Wrasse
Labrichthys unilineatus

Lives in rich coral reefs from silty lagoons to outer reef crests, often swimming through large branching staghorn corals. Males greenish and usually show a large pale area on the body just behind the head. Juveniles black with a white mid-lateral line. Common in the Maldives. Widespread Indo-Pacific, some geographical variations between oceans. Indian Ocean fish grow larger and have proportionally much longer ventral fins, and Pacific fish are more blue.
Length to 20 cm.
Photo, juvenile: Jörg Aebi.

LUNATE-TAILED WRASSES - LABRIDAE-4

This group includes the genus *Thalassoma*, usually round-headed fish that swim strongly with their pectoral fins, and the long-snouted *Gomphosus* that is closely related. Their pectoral fins, directly situated behind the short head, often feature bright colours in the male. The tail in adults become strongly lunate and this is often accentuated by part of the fin being clear or development of long fin tips. Some other wrasses have lunate tails, but usually not as a distinctive feature. Some juveniles and females school. Males are often solitary but in some species they may share reef flats and regularly fight. Diet comprises a great variety of creatures that are picked from the bottom as well as plankton. Mainly opportunity feeders and some species follow other fishes that disturb the sand, such as goatfishes, to grab an easy prey. Colour changes between juveniles and sexes are gradual and not as dramatic as in most other wrasses.

Bird Wrasse
Gomphosus caeruleus

Mainly on shallow reef crests, but often along the top of deep walls. Unusual member of this group in having a greatly extended snout when adult. In small juveniles the snout is relatively short. Commonly found in the Maldives, swimming in rich coral growth, usually several females and a male nearby. Colour variable between different stages, easily identified by the long snout. Indian Ocean only, replaced by the similar *G. varius* east of Java, Indonesia.
Length to 25 cm.
Photo, juvenile: Java, Indonesia.

Two-tone Wrasse
Thalassoma amblycephalum

Juveniles and females form large groups, each of individuals of similar size, that roam reef flats, often in shallow turbulent surge zones. Males venture down to at least 30 m depth. Feeds on plankton as well as bottom creatures. Slender species, males variable, head usually green. Juveniles white with a broad black stripe on sides and over back. Widespread Indo-Pacific.
Length to 16 cm.
Photo, juveniles: Sulawesi, Indonesia.

Six-bar Wrasse
Thalassoma hardwicke

Shallow to deep drop-offs but usually swim along the top of reefs in small loose groups. Common in the Maldives and often follows divers in case they disturb the bottom, ready to crab unsuspected prey. Pale green with series of dark-green to pink, or black saddles over back. Juveniles more banded. widespread Indo-Pacific.
Length to 20 cm.
Photo, juvenile: Neville Coleman.

Jansen's Wrasse *Thalassoma janseni*

In the Maldives this species seems to prefer surge zones adjacent to outer reef walls and are commonly seen in gutters to 10 m depth. They occur in small aggregations with a large male in charge. Mainly black, head half-white below and white extending along and tapering away below anal fin. Males turn-on pale yellow bands. Widespread Indo-Pacific, but several geographical variations. Length to 20 cm.

Moon Wrasse
Thalassoma lunare

Various habitats from shallow lagoons to outer reef walls to about 35 m depth. Usually in small groups and can become very inquisitive toward divers. Males variable from dark green to bright blue and pink bands radiating from eye, tail fin often yellow. Juveniles green to brown and large round spot in dorsal fin. Common throughout Indo-Pacific. Length to 22 cm.
Photo, juvenile: Toshikazu Kozawa.

Red-ribbon Wrasse
Thalassoma quinquevittatum

Common in the Maldives but prefers shallow surge zones where few divers go. Especially likes areas where coral plates (*Acropora*) are prolific and some algae growth below, with reef channels and rubble areas. Usually in depths between 6 and 10 m. Males swim quickly over large areas of reef. Identified by the red or deep pink bands on the cheek that are absent in similar species. Widespread Indo-Pacific. Length to 15 cm.

Surge Wrasse
Thalassoma purpureum

A flighty species that lives almost exclusively in the shallow surge zone that typically features on the outer reefs of the Maldives. Rarely seen in depths over 10 m. Usually occurs in groups of females and sometimes several males. Male identified by green cheek and large size. One of the largest in the genus but also the most shy, a challenge to a fish photographer. Widespread Indo-Pacific. Length to 25 cm.
Photo, female: Bali, Indonesia.

A large group of mostly small-sized planktivorous wrasses, but only a few of which known from the Maldives. The majority of species are less than 10 cm long, fully grown. In interesting feature is a divided eye-cornea that enable them to focus separately on tiny prey in front of the mouth, besides normal viewing. Most males have fancy colours that are used to display to females or other males, and swimming about frantically. In many species the brightest colours are in the fins that are suddenly erected to have the greatest impact, some are known as 'flasher wrasses'. Where common, adults form large schools and feed on plankton high above reefs or well away from walls, usually during currents. Small groups are often along reef edges above rubble bottom where they sleep and in the evening they are often seen swimming in and out small holes to check them for safety. Small juveniles are more secretive on coral rubble. Most juveniles in species of the genera *Cirrhilabrus* and *Paracheilinus* look alike, typically brown with a white tipped nose. Genus *Cirrhilabrus* has over 30 species, 2 of which known from the Maldives; *Paracheilinus* about 10 species, 1 in the Maldives; and *Pseudocheilinus* has 6 species, 3 of which known from the Maldives.

Exquisite Wrasse *Cirrhilabrus exquisitus*

Found on shallow reef crests to deep bommies on sand flats to at least 40 m depth. The only common species in the Maldives. Males often in small groups, busy displaying to each other. Displaying males show blue spots and lines, pink on face and yellow to orange tail. Juveniles are brown, changing to green with growth. Widespread Indo-Pacific, but Pacific form is quite different and may warrant separate species status. Length to 11 cm.

Rosy-scaled Wrasse
Cirrhilabrus rubrisquamis

Mainly found along drop-offs in invertebrate rich habitats with caves and ledges to at least 50 m depth. Primarily a deep water species but female was photographed shallow. Sometimes in small groups on rubble patches below reef overhangs. Generally light pink all over and scales on front half of body with dark pink edges. Females with thin whitish lines running along upper sides. Only known from the Maldives and Chagos Archipelago.
Length to 65 mm.
Photo, top-left, male: Mustag Hussain; top-right, female: Toshikazu Kozawa; bottom, displaying male: Jörg Aebi.

McCosker's Wrasse *Paracheilinus mccoskeri*

Small groups are usually found on rubble on sand along the bottom of reefs in 20+ m depth. Single males are usually seen displaying to the females only. They swim lower the bottom than other similar species. They rise only short distances above the substrate when feeding on zooplankton. Males readily identified by extended ray on dorsal fin. Indian Ocean species, doubtfully ranging to Indonesia. Pacific siblings considerably different in colour: males with yellow anal fin, and usually have a double extended ray on the back fin.
Length to 65 mm. Photo, juvenile, right: Toshikazu Kozawa; displaying male, left: Jörg Aebi.

Pin-striped Wrasse
Pseudocheilinus evanidus

A secretive small species that swims between rubble and corals to hunt small prey. Moderately common in the Maldives on shallow protected reefs but ranges to deep water along walls with rubble patches below large overhangs to at least 40 m depth. Orange to pink-brown in colour, sometimes faintly banded, best identified by whitish streak from mouth along cheek. Widespread Indo-Pacific. Length to 8 cm.

Eight-line Wrasse
Pseudocheilinus octotaenia

Clear inner to outer reef habitats. Usually in moderate depths along drop-offs on the bottom of large caves with rich invertebrate growth. Widespread Indo-Pacific.
Length to 12 cm.
Photo: Manado, Indonesia.

Six-line Wrasse
Pseudocheilinus hexataenia

A common and colourful small fish that swims in rich coral areas and rubble reef, often in small groups. Remains in coverage of reefs but very active and often noticed by divers. Depth range 3 to 20 m, rarely deeper. Readily identified by mauve body with many orange lines, sometimes greenish above. Widespread Indo-Pacific.
Length to 60 mm in the Maldives, 85 mm in Indonesia.

CAVE WRASSES - LABRIDAE-6

A small group of interesting little fishes that have adapted to living in the back of dark caves. Divers need to use a torch to find them, but have to be on the look-out for them as they don't like the light and quickly hide. Turning off the light will bring them back and when getting used to the dim light they can be observed. They usually occur in pairs, using the various holes and tunnels in the back of caves to move about, picking tiny prey from the bottom. A single genus and two of the known three species occur in the Maldives, and both are common there.

White-banded Possum Wrasse *Wetmorella albofasciata*

Inner and outer reefs, along walls in the back of large caves and over-hangs at all divable depths. The white radiating lines from the eye, identifies this species. The lines crossing the body are always white and the one before the tail is at an angle. Widespread Indo-Pacific. Length to 55 mm.

Yellow-banded Possum Wrasse *Wetmorella nigropinnata*

Found in caves in deep lagoons as well as outer reef walls. Adults usually occur in pairs and juveniles singly. Juveniles and females have four white bands but males loose their central body bands and the remaining two turn yellow. Widespread Indo-Pacific. Length to 65 mm.

MAORI AND THICKLIP WRASSES - LABRIDAE-7

This groups includes the largest wrasses. Generally the large scaled and thick-lipped species that associate with reefs. Many are noticed by divers because of size and behaviour, especially the Napoleon fish that easily gets accustomed to divers. There are some problems with regards to some of the scientific names of the smaller *Cheilinus* species and the genus is in need of revision. Recent authors use *Oxycheilinus* for the more slender species. Most species are seen solitary in various habitats of the reef. Small species stay close to the bottom and the large ones often swim in open waters well away from reefs. Small juveniles of most species are very secretive and rarely seen, either living amongst rubble or weeds. They sleep in narrow crevices or caves. Diet comprises small invertebrates but some species prey primarily on juvenile fishes. Genus *Epibulus* has one wide-spread species, possible second one from Philippines to eastern Papua New Guinea; *Cheilinus* has 7 species, 5 of which in the Maldives; *Oxycheilinus* about 10 species, but taxonomic problems and some undescribed, 4 of which in the Maldives; and *Hemigymnus* has 2 species, both in the Maldives.

Sling-jaw wrasse *Epibulus insidiator*

Lagoon and protected reefs to about 20 m depth. Mouth greatly extendable to catch prey. Small juveniles secretive in corals and look remarkably like possum wrasses or small juvenile banded maori wrasses. Variable in colour, sometimes bright yellow all over, best recognised by the unusually shaped mouth that is expendable into a suction tube. A common species in the Maldives. Widespread Indo-Pacific. Length to 30 cm.

Banded Maori Wrasse *Cheilinus fasciatus*

Inhabits lagoons and inner reefs, usually swims along reef margins over rubble zones to depths of at least 30 m. Identified by the broadly banded pattern over the body. Small juveniles in corals and look remarkably like possum wrasses. Males with large red area over head and extended lobes on the tail. Widespread Indo-Pacific. Length to 35 cm. Photo, juvenile: Java, Indonesia.

Triple-tail Maori Wrasse *Cheilinus trilobatus*

Adults mainly shallow protected reefs to about 10 m depth, often in silty inshore conditions. Juveniles in algae reef habitat. Usually seen singly but occasionally occurs in loose groups. Adults develop long tips on the tail fin and are identified by the fine pink spotting and scribbles over the head. Juveniles with numerous thin vertical lines and series of dark spots mid-laterally towards tail. Widespread Indo-Pacific. Length to 40 cm.

White-dotted Maori Wrasse *Cheilinus chlorourus*

Mainly found in shallow lagoons and harbours on rubble or around bommies. Adults occur in small loose groups dominated by a large male, juveniles singly in corals. Can be identified by the white spots on the body, usually one on each scale and often with series of white saddles over the back. Common in the Maldives. Widespread Indo-Pacific. Length to 35 cm.

Napoleonfish
Cheilinus undulatus

Best known member in the genus. Large males with the humped head are favourite with many divers, and they can be seen swimming singly along deep walls and often are resident on shipwrecks. Small juveniles live in weedy areas and are rarely seen. Generally a greenish colour and a dark vertical bar on each scale forming vertical lines. Widespread Indo-Pacific.
Length to 2 m. Photo, full framed individual: Bali, Indonesia; juvenile, below: Java, Indonesia.

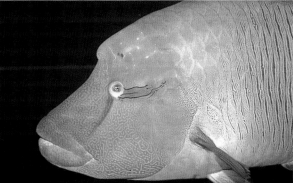

Point-head Maori Wrasse
Cheilinus oxycephalus

A small secretive species in lagoons and reef crests, swimming amongst corals and rarely out in the open. Variable from greenish grey to brownish red and adults usually with fine white speckles over the head. Deep bodied for genus and snout pointed. Common in the Maldives but easily overlooked. Widespread Indo-Pacific.
Length to 17 cm.

Cheek-line Maori Wrasse
Oxycheilinus digrammus

Usually seen solitary and often swimming high above the bottom. Occurs on almost every reef habitat to depths of about 30 m. Pale green to reddish brown, males with pink scribbles on head, many obliquely on cheek. Sometime curious towards divers. Moderately common in the Maldives. Widespread Indo-Pacific.
Length to 35 cm.

Oriental Maori Wrasse
Oxycheilinus notophthalmus

Previously known as *Cheilinus orientalis*. Found mainly on clear water reefs and along drop-offs to 45 m depth. Small juveniles often in crinoid featherstars or black coral bushes. Similar to Cheek-line Maori Wrasse but usually show a broad dark band along the body and is much smaller. Widespread Indo-Pacific.
Length to 20 cm.
Photo, juvenile: Bali, Indonesia.

Thin-line Maori Wrasse
Oxycheilinus arenatus

A deep water species, occasionally seen along outer reef walls in rich invertebrate habitats with soft corals and seawhips, usually over 20 m depth. Appears to live solitary but little known about this species. Identified by the pale body and the thin reddish mid-lateral line along the sides. Indian ocean and ranges to the west Pacific.
Length to 15 cm.
Photo: Flores, Indonesia.

Little Maori Wrasse
Oxycheilinus bimaculatus

One of the smallest in the genus. In the Maldives mainly in shallow surge-zones with algae good growth or deep on rubble with algae cover. Males develop filaments on the tail, at the tips and in centre. Colours variable from green to brown red. Widespread Indo-Pacific. Length to 15 cm, but in the Maldives the largest seen about 10 cm.
Photo, female: Jörg Aebi.
Photo, displaying male: Bali, Indonesia.

Banded Thicklip Wrasse *Hemigymnus fasciatus*

Adults often in small loose groups in shallow depth on reef crests and slopes. Juveniles secretive in rubble reef, small ones often amongst urchin spines. Variable in colour from green to black, body always banded. Male changes colour on the face during courtship, showing black horse-shoe shaped mark on cheek. Widespread Indo-Pacific. Length to 30 cm. Photo, juvenile: Bali, Indonesia.

Half-and-Half Wrasse *Hemigymnus melapterus*

Occurs on most reef habitats. Juveniles secretive in rubble reefs, adults swim openly over reefs. Surprisingly shy in the Maldives compared to elsewhere. Photographs, at close range, could only be taken where they were used to divers. Small juveniles green with broad white band centrally, changing front half white with abrupt change to black on back half and yellow to orange tail. Adults mainly spotted. Common in the Maldives. Widespread Indo-Pacific. Length to 50 cm.

The hogfishes are the most wide-ranging among wrasses, some species living in temperate waters, but most are absent from oceanic locations or represent a different species. Only two species are commonly encountered in the Maldives, both wide-ranging in the Indian Ocean. Juveniles often engage in cleaning activities, often working in small groups in caves or around coral bommies. Diet comprises small shelled invertebrates, especially shrimps, but also worms. The genus *Bodianus* comprises about 35 species, 4 of which known in the Maldives. Some species are restricted to very deep water and could occur in the Maldives. The related large genus *Choerodon* is completely absent and appears to be restricted to continental waters. A new, second species of the only recently described genus *Terelabrus* was photographed by Jörg Aebi.

Diana Hogfish *Bodianus diana*

Occurs on shallow reef crests as well as deep along walls to at least 50 m depth. Juveniles regularly clean other fishes from parasites. Reddish to dark brown with series of pale yellow or white spots. Large adults with red fins. The most common hogfish in the Maldives. Indian Ocean only, ranging east to Java, Indonesia. Replaced by sibling Pacific species in Bali and rest of Pacific, yet to be named. Length to 25 cm.

Coral Hogfish
Bodianus axillaris

Also known as Axilspot Hogfish. Usually seen solitary, swimming through reefs in caves or overhangs along slopes and walls. Sometimes shallow, but usually between 10 and 30 m depth. The white-spotted black females get large in the Maldives compared to other areas, eventually changing to the half-dark and half-light male pattern. Common in the Maldives. Widespread Indo-Pacific Length to 20 cm.

Lyre-tail Hogfish *Bodianus anthioides*

Mainly occurs on coral rich reefs along walls adjacent to deep water. Usually solitary, swimming close to reef in 10 to 40 m depth. Small juveniles in large black coral bushes sponges. Easily identified by distinctive colour pattern. Widespread Indo-Pacific. Length to 22 cm. Photo, small juvenile: Bali, Indonesia; adult: Jörg Aebi.

Saddle-back Hogfish *Bodianus bilunulatus*

Outer reef habitat, usually at moderate depths. Rare in the Maldives and probably deep compared to continental waters. Juveniles in rich rubble zones on deep slopes. Widespread Indo-Pacific. Some geographical variations. Length to 40 cm.

Yellow Hogfish *Bodianus bimaculatus*

Usually on rubble patches on the bottom of large overhangs along walls, in depths in excess of 40 m. Swims in small groups close to the bottom. A small deep water species, occurring in different depths in other areas. In Bali, Indonesia, as shallow as 20 m, whilst in most other areas only below 40 m. Identified by bright yellow colour, males with thin orange lines. Uncommon in the Maldives. Indo-Pacific.
Length to 10 cm, usually much smaller, about 6 cm.
Photo: Jörg Aebi.

Red-lined Hogfish *Terelabrus* sp.

A new discovery in the Maldives. Its Pacific sibling, *T. rubrovittatus,* which is reddish in colour with a yellow line, was only recently described as a new genus and species. Most specimens were found in depths in excess of 60 m.
Length to about 10 cm.
Photo: Jörg Aebi.

PARROTFISHES - SCARIDAE

Large tropical family with 9 genera and about 80 species globally, 23 of which recorded from the Maldives. They are amongst the most noticed fishes on reefs, because of their large size and bright colours. Some are common and by eating the algae and hard coral materials they contribute greatly to the reef building process. This becomes evident when discharging the processed matter in a cloud on white dust that sinks to the bottom. Adults often school and feed together on shallow reef flats on high tides. They travel along reef edges, some moving over considerably great distances between feeding sites during the day and sleeping places at night. Juveniles are solitary or form small groups, depending on the species. Seagrass species commonly form large schools at all sizes. Colour can change dramatically with growth or between sexes and often the only way to connect their stages to a species is by seeing intermediates or interaction between male and female. Females are usually in their own schools and spawning activities are near dusk. Typically groups gathering at reef corners where eggs and sperm is released simultaneously near the surface at out-going tides. Diet comprises algae, seagrasses or other vegetation and some species additionally take invertebrates, including coral polyps.

Two-colour Parrotfish
Cetoscarus bicolor

Occurs along reef slopes and upper parts of drop-offs, from shallows to about 30 m. Juveniles and sexes differ considerably from each other. Juveniles solitary in rich coral growth, lagoons to outer reefs. Adult males usually on reef slopes on outer reefs. Juveniles readily identified by the white body and orange band over the head. Males bright green with pink markings. Common in the Maldives. Widespread Indo-Pacific.
Length to 90 cm.

Humphead Parrotfish
Bolbometopon muricatum

A schooling species, often seen
travelling in close packs along reef
slopes and edges, occasionally
stopping for a feeding session on
coral heads. Dull greenish grey,
large adults develop a large hump
on their head. Sleep in caves and
crevices in reefs or shipwrecks at
night in a bout 15 to 30 m depth.
Widespread Indo-Pacific. Largest
parrotfish, length to 1.2 m.
Photos: Bali, Indonesia.

Longnose Parrotfish
Hipposcarus harid

Deep lagoons to outer reefs. Males
usually seen solitary and females
in small groups. Juveniles secretive in staghorn corals in lagoons,
and they are recognised by the red
stripe centrally along their sides.
Adults are best identified by the
long shape of their snout. Inner
reefs and lagoons, often in silty
reefs. West Indian Ocean and Red
Sea. Its sibling *H. longiceps* in
Pacific.
Length to 60 cm.

Sheephead Parrotfish
Scarus strongylocephalus

Commonly occurs in inner reef crests with rich coral growth and rubble zones, often females in small groups with large male nearby. Female has distinctive colouration and male is best identified by head shape and colours around eye and on cheek. Widespread Indian Ocean, ranging to southern Java, Indonesia. Replaced by *S. microrhinos* in Pacific. Length to 70 cm.

Ember Parrotfish
Scarus rubroviolaceus

Mainly found along deep slopes and drop-offs on inner to outer reefs, often openly swimming in groups. To depths of about 35 m. Females are distinctly marked, males are best identified by the shape of the snout and head colouration. Widespread Indo-Pacific, juveniles expatriate into sub-tropical waters. Length to 70 cm.

Bridled Parrotfish
Scarus frenatus

Reef slopes and drop-offs, mainly outer reef habitats. Males usually seen solitary and females may form small groups, sometimes mixing with other species. Males distinguished by the head colour and abrupt body colour change to the pale green that continues on to the tail, and females by the brown to pink fins. Widespread Indo-Pacific. Length to 47 cm, usually much smaller. Photo above, juvenile: Jörg Aebi.

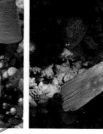

Shabby Parrotfish *Scarus sordidus*

Various reef habitats, adults mainly on clear inner and outer reef slopes and along top of deep drop-offs. Juveniles from seagrass beds and shallow lagoons to protected inner algae reefs, forming small groups. Colour patterns readily identifies both sexes. Widespread Indo-Pacific. Length to 40 cm.

Five-saddle Parrotfish *Scarus scaber*

Commonly occurs in large lagoons with coral slopes and on inner reefs, often in silty conditions. Usually in small groups of mixed sexes. Readily identified by colour patterns, distinct in both sexes. West Indian Ocean. Length to 35 cm. Similar *S. dimidiatus* in the Pacific.

Three-colour Parrotfish
Scarus tricolor

Commonly occurs along deep outer reef walls and clear inner reef slopes. Usually in moderate depths from 10 to 40 m. Males identified by the long green stripes over the head, usually short in similar species. Female has dark body, sometimes almost black, yellow eye, and pinkish brown tail. Widespread equatorial waters of Indo-Pacific.
Length to 40 cm.

Rosy-cheek Parrotfish *Scarus psittacus*

Various reef habitats from silty inshore reef to outer reef walls. Highly variable, male usually with yellow along the base of the dorsal fin on the back. Cheek mostly pink and in the Maldives males often bright yellow over the back. Widespread Indo-Pacific. One of the smallest species, length to 30 cm.

Green-face Parrotfish
Scarus prasiognathus

A common species on outer reef slopes, often in large groups of females as well as males. Latter easily recognised by the bright green on the cheek and snout. Females are dark with white spotting as shown in the photograph. Mainly Indian Ocean, but ranging along continent to southern Japan.
Length to 60 cm.
Photo, male: Neville Coleman.

Dusky Parrotfish
Scarus niger

Clear inner reef crests to outer reef drop-offs at various depths to about 30 m. Males look very dark in natural light and have a distinctive green band behind the eye. Females are reddish brown below and the sides bear a lined pattern. However, colour patterns with regards to lines and band behind eye varies greatly throughout its Indo-Pacific range. Length to 40 cm.

Green-snout Parrotfish *Scarus viridifucatus*

Inshore reefs and clear lagoons with rich coral and rubble zones, usually seen solitary on reef crests or swimming with other species to feed together. Females dark and very plain but males distinctive by the large green patch around the mouth, almost reaching eyes. Widespread Indian Ocean, ranging to Bali and Sulawesi, Indonesia. Length to 25 cm.

Green-blotched Parrotfish
Scarus quoyi

Inshore species, primarily found on reef crests and slopes, occasionally outer reefs, often in silty habitat where forming large schools of mixed sexes. Males identified by almost entire purplish head with green around the mouth, extending in a band to the eye. Widespread Indo-Pacific.
Length to 40 cm.

Black-tip Parrotfish *Scarus capistratoides*

Clear inner to outer reef crests with coral boulders rich with algae growth, usually shallow in surge zones. Females broadly banded and pectoral fins yellow. Males with pinks bars on most body scales and green short lines above, below and behind eyes. One of a complex of similar species, probably widespread Indian Ocean, ranging to Bali, Indonesia. Length to 40 cm. Photos: Bali, Indonesia.

Bartail Parrotfish
Scarus caudofasciatus

Clear outer reef habitats, usually in depths over 20 m, males rather flighty. Distinctly patterned female of broad white band on back half of body, males mainly green with thick blue stripes over snout and along fin margins, and long lobes on tail fin. Only known from western Indian Ocean.
Length to 50 cm.
Photo, male: Charles Anderson.

Eclipse Parrotfish
Scarus russelli

Commonly found on outer reef slopes in 6 to 15 m depth, usually near edge of deep water. Males solitary and large individuals are distinctive by the yellow patch following the mouth, and half dark - half light body colour. Females banded. Only known from the west Indian Ocean. Length to 50 cm.

Happy Parrotfish *Scarus festivus*

Clear water reefs, mainly inner reefs. Uncommon in the Maldives, but an inconspicuous species until fully grown male that has a rather blunt head and distinctive banding over the top above eyes, and below the mouth towards the eye. Widespread Indo-Pacific, but mainly continental waters of Asia, ranging to southern Japan. Length to 45 cm.
Photo: Kerama, Japan.

Blue-barred Parrotfish
Scarus ghobban

Inshore reefs but adults usually in moderate depths of 15 to 40 m depth where common and sometimes in small groups. Juveniles on algae reef habitat and are similar to the adults, but banding more pronounced and usually showing following twin white spots on the sides in the Indian Ocean population. Widespread Indo-Pacific.
Length to 75 cm

Spinytooth Parrotfish *Calotomus spinidens*

Inshore habitat, usually in seagrass habitat channels or adjacent slopes to about 25 m depth. Often swims amongst weeds and is well camouflaged. Eats seagrasses and algae, including invertebrates living on them. Brownish or green with two series of spaced white spots along upper sides. Widespread Indo-Pacific. Length to about 30 cm.
Photo: Papua New Guinea.

Starry-eye Parrotfish *Calotomus carolinus*

Inner to outer reef crest in channels and around large coral heads. Dull looking species, usually not noticed. Males dusky grey-brown, greenish over back, and with red lines radiating from eyes. Mainly scrapes algae from dead coral bases. Widespread Indo-Pacific. Length to 40 cm.

Seagrass Parrotfish *Leptoscarus vaigiensis*

Commonly occurs in seagrass beds, usually very shallow intertidal zones, swimming in groups during feeding sessions, mainly consuming seagrass leaves including algae and invertebrate growth on it. Mainly green, males with white mid-lateral line. Widespread Indo-Pacific. Length to 35 cm.
Photo: Neville Coleman.

GRUBFISHES - PINGUIPEDIDAE

A moderately large mostly tropical family with at least 4 genera and 60+ species, four of which known from the Maldives. They are called sandsmelts in Africa, and also known as weevers or sand perches elsewhere, but don't look like smelts or perches. These bottom fishes are commonly seen on or near reefs, especially rubble zones. Tropical species are found on shallow reef crests and slopes, but in cool temperate seas most occur very deep and are only known from trawls. Some of the reef species have very similar colouration and can be difficult to identify. Several species appear to be undescribed. The adult and juvenile stages are very similar and differences between sexes are small, usually some additional markings on the cheek or lips of the male. Grubfishes are diurnal and dig the sand under solid pieces or reef to make shelter to escape danger or to sleep. Diet comprises small animals and zooplankton.

Maldivian Grubfish *Parapercis signata*

Clear sand habitat in lagoons and sand flats along reef edges, near large remote coral heads, on rubble or sand to at least 50 m depth. Usually small groups spread out in the area and occasionally pairing. Colouration distinctive, sandy and first dorsal fin dark. Only known from the Maldives where common.
Length to 13 cm.

Black-tail Grubfish *Parapercis hexophthalma*

Occurs in large sandy lagoons and open sand slopes between reefs, including silty habitat. Usually shallow to about 15 m depth. Small juveniles have an almost fully black tail, reducing from the margins to a proportionally smaller area in adults. Body very pale with series of small dark spots, lowest series black and more defined. Widespread Indo-Pacific.
Length to 25 cm.

Thousand-spot Grubfish *Parapercis millipunctata*

Commonly found on algae reefs with mixed sand and coarse rubble from lagoons to outer reef slopes in very shallow water to about 15 m depth. In the Maldives this species is distinctive by the series of dark blotches along the body and the white streak in the tail fin. Elsewhere several similar species. Widespread west Pacific, ranging into Indian Ocean as far as Maldives. Length to 14 cm.

Lyre-tail Grubfish
Parapercis schauinslandi

A rare species in the Maldives and only a few seen in deep water, at 35 m, sandy channel with rubble bottom. Often swims well above the bottom to feed in currents on zooplankton. Tail is very distinctive with the elongated tips. Generally in depths of 10 to at least 50 m, often occurs in small groups. Widespread Indo-Pacific, common in Indonesia.
Length to 18 cm.
Photo top: Jörg Aebi; lower, adult: male: Bali, Indonesia.

SAND DIVERS - TRICHONOTIDAE

A small Indo-Pacific family with a single genus and at least 8 species, one of which known from the Maldives, but more to be expected. Typically occur in groups on sand slopes with slow tidal currents and feed on zooplankton at particular times. Quickly dives into the sand when approached.

Long-rayed Sand Diver
Trichonotus elegans

Clear water sand slopes, seen in the Maldives between 5 and 20 m depth. Swims in large groups, often many males together, displaying to each other with the long filaments in the dorsal fin. The smaller females and juveniles swim closely together when feeding. When no current is running, they are usually all buried in the sand slopes. A widespread species, originally described from Japan but occurs commonly throughout Indonesia and photographs represent first record for the Maldives.
Length to 18 cm, usually about 15 cm.

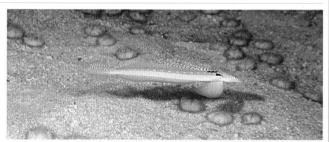

TRIPLEFINS - TRIPTERYGIIDAE

A large family of mostly small tropical fishes (some grow much larger in sub-tropical seas) with over 20, perhaps 30 genera and probably about 200 species. Most species are undescribed and because of small size and similarly camouflaged colours are difficult to work on. These blenny related fishes are characterised by three separate dorsal fins. They are also known as threefins. Sometimes the male displays bright colours prior to spawning and a few have permanent distinctive colouration. Most species are a few centimetres long and live among algal reef habitats in crevices of cave walls. Possibly about 10 species in the Maldives but few are commonly observed and only two included here. Their diet comprises small animals, benthic and zooplankton.

Maldives Triplefin *Helcogramma maldivensis*

Clear water reefs, often on coral outcrops along steep slopes or drop-offs in depths from about 6 to 35 m. Often in small groups on sponges or smooth corals. One of the few easily recognised species from distinctive colouration of stripes and spots. Only known from Maldives and Sri Lanka. Length to 40 mm.

Green-head Triplefin
Helcogramma sp.

Undetermined species. Sheltered reefs, usually on the bases of corals or in caves along slopes and drop-offs in algae. There are many similar species in this genus and of the well over one hundred estimated species, several can be expected in the Maldives, most of which are undescribed.
Length of this species, about 40 mm.
Photo: Toshikazu Kozawa.

BLENNIES - BLENNIIDAE

A very large family, comprises several distinctive groups or sub-families with more than 50 genera and about 350 species globally. They are divided here into two groups, the free-swimming, and those usually resting on the bottom.

SABRETOOTH BLENNIES - BLENNIIDAE-1

A group of slender and usually boldly marked species that swim above the bottom when in pursuit of food. They retreat to holes in the reef to escape danger, for nesting, or to sleep. The sabretooth blennies have long sabre-like teeth in their lower jaw, venomous in some, that point forward when the mouth is wide open. Some harmless fishes, including some other blennies, mimic the venomous species that are respected by predators that target small fishes. Diet comprises various zooplankton and some specialise in feeding on parts of other fishes as explained in species accounts.

Smith's Venomous Blenny
Meiacanthus smithi

Sheltered clear reef habitats with large coral rubble with mixed algae and coral growth, and soft bottom habitat with sponges and rich invertebrate growth. Usually seen solitary, shallow to depths of 35 m. Feeds on small invertebrates. Widespread Indian Ocean from Maldives to southern Indonesia.
Length to 75 mm.

Imposter Blenny
Plagiotremus phenax

Sheltered reef habitat, usually shallow on reef flats with large corals. Mimics *Meiacanthus smithi* and is easily overlooked. Best distinguished by the lack of the stripe from the eye that is distinct in the *Meiacanthus*. Attacks other fishes, biting fins and scales. Widespread Indian Ocean from Maldives to southern Indonesia.
Length to 60 mm.

Mimic Blenny
Plagiotremus tapeinosoma

Also known as Piano Blenny. Seen singly or in small numbers, but often swims with similar shaped planktivores and attacks large fishes that swim close by. Takes bites from fins, scales or mucus, in a 'hit and run' fashion, quickly disappearing in the reef when chased by an angry victim. Also bites divers, especially snorkelers going up to the surface. Shallow protected reefs. Widespread Indo-Pacific.
Length to 12 cm.

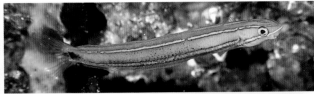

Tube-worm Blenny
Plagiotremus rhinorhynchos

A moderately common species along inner reef slopes with mixed algae and coral growth. Uses empty tubeworm shells in the reef for shelter and nesting. Male guards eggs, entices female to nest by courting in a dance like motion, but gets rather rough, as female often bares scars. Variable in colour from orange to almost black with two blue lines. Widespread Indo-Pacific.
Length to 12 cm.

False Cleanerfish
Aspidontus taeniatus

Sheltered reef slopes and crests, usually in mixed invertebrate and algae habitat. Adults usually in small aggregations, feeding on the bottom. Juveniles, until almost fully grown, solitary and busy impersonating the cleaner wrasse *Labroides dimidiatus*. Unlike the cleaner wrasses that takes parasites from other fishes, the blenny bites bits of the fins such as fins. Large adults do this part time only, feeding mainly on the reef itself on invertebrates and algae. Widespread Indo-Pacific.
Length to 12 cm.
Photo, lower: Jörg Aebi.

Lance Blenny *Aspidontus dussumieri*

Rare in the Maldives. Mainly inshore and often silty habitat with rocky algae reefs, on crests and slopes, usually solitary, in depths to 20 m. Identified by the long body and smooth black stripe along upper sides. Sometimes has filaments on the tail fin. Uses empty tubeworm tubes for shelter. Feeds on zooplankton and may bite other fishes. Widespread Indo-Pacific. Length to 12 cm. Photo left: Australia, close-up: Bali, Indonesia.

Crested Sabretooth Blenny
Petroscirtes mitratus

Only found on seagrass beds and reef with heavy algae or sargassum growth, but common in those habitats in the Maldives. Often rests against seagrass leaves and sometimes seen floating along, suspended in the water column, with the tail curled in. Recognised by the dorsal tall fin, closely behind the head, and leafy bits above the eyes. Widespread Indo-Pacific. Length to 65 mm.

Bearded Sabretooth Blenny
Petroscirtes xestus

Mainly found on silty reefs and commonly occurs in harbours and lagoons on rubble reef, seeking refuge in small holes or crevices. Recognised by the pale colour, thin dark line, and leafy bits on the chin. Widespread Indo-Pacific.
Length to 65 mm.

REEF BLENNIES - BLENNIIDAE-2

The largest group of blennies are bottom dwellers in shallow coastal waters, some intertidal and may be left high and dry for a short time as the water level drops from the swell or wave action. Most reef or rock blennies are territorial and as they scrape algae for food of dead coral surfaces, each has its own little patch. Often they occur in spread out groups and males may allow some females nearby but females often argue amongst themselves. There are many species-complexes that represent geographical forms, especially among the combtooth blennies. The similar species in such a group can be difficult to distinguish from each other. Amongst rock blennies, males may have different colour patterns from females, and in some species males develop a crest on the head.

Black-eared Eyelash Blenny
Cirripectes auritus

Clear water inner reef crests and slopes in rich coral habitat, usually shallow in 6 to 10 m depth. Pale creamy brown and easily identified by the 'ear' spot. Moderately common in the Maldives. Widespread Indo-Pacific.
Length to 9 cm.

Chestnut Eyelash Blenny
Cirripectes castaneus

Very common in the Maldives on inner and outer reef crests, rarely deeper than 6 m. Looks dusky and almost featureless with some indistinct barring, but tail fin often yellowish. Widespread Indo-Pacific.
Length to 12 cm.

Red-streaked Eyelash Blenny
Cirripectes stigmaticus

Reef crests with rich coral growth, especially large *Acropora* plate corals where males can sit boldly out in the open, but ready to dive for cover when approached, or by the first sign of trouble. Only males are easily identified by the red vertical streaks on their sides, females plain dark. Widespread Indo-Pacific.
Length to 10 cm. Photo: Bali, Indonesia.

Little Combtooth Blenny
Ecsenius minutus

Common on clear inner and outer reef slopes, usually found on corals or around the bases to about 10 m depth. Identified by the series of pale spots along the body. Only known from the Maldives. Belongs to a species-complex distributed throughout the Indo-Pacific.
Length to 65 mm.
Photo above, baby: Toshikazu Kozawa.

Two-colour Combtooth Blenny
Ecsenius bicolor

Clear water reef crests and slopes, and in outer reef lagoons with coral bommies to about 20 m depth. Two colour forms: half orange and half black, or a black top with white belly. Apparently the different colour forms are not sex related. Widespread Indo-Pacific.
Length to 85 mm.

Lined Combtooth Blenny
Ecsenius lineatus

A common species in the Maldives. Various reef habitats, mainly sheltered deep lagoons on remote coral heads to depths of at least 30 m. Variable from very dark banded to the band broken up into series of spots. Latter variation common in the Maldives. Widespread Indo-Pacific. Length to 10 cm.
Photo, top-right, spotted form: Mustag Hussain.

Lyre-tail Combtooth Blenny *Ecsenius midas*

Inner to outer reef habitats on coral slopes in current prone areas. Has unusual behaviour for its genus: swims high above the bottom when current is running to feed on zooplankton. The blennies often mix with orange or yellow basslets and take on the same colour, becoming 'one of the pack'. They retreat to reefs and use small holes to reverse themselves in to. Often seen with just the head at the entrance. Identified by shape and colour, the lyre-shaped tail is diagnostic. Widespread Indo-Pacific, some colour variations in different areas. Length to 13 cm.

Leopard Blenny *Exallias brevis*

Usually found in rich coral reef crests, sitting on top of *Acropora* thickets and quickly disappear when approached. Often occur in small loose groups but usually only the larger dominating one moves about openly. In depths of about 6 m and males prepare base of coral as nesting site. Widespread Indo-Pacific. Length to 14 cm. Photo left, pinkish male: Jörg Aebi; right, black-spotted: Neville Coleman.

Jewelled Blenny
Salarias fasciatus

Not common in the Maldives, mainly found in still highly protected shallow reefs and harbours amongst dead coral rubble. Elsewhere in coastal reef habitats to about 10 m depth. Appears to be deep-bodied because of tall and long-based dorsal fins. Has a pattern of dark blotches and striations. Widespread Indo-Pacific with some geographical variations.
Length to 14 cm.

Big-nose Blenny
Entomacrodus striatus

Silty reefs, inshore, often on shallow beams below jetties near the surface. Occurs in small groups, dominated by the largest individuals. A large bushy tentacle above the eye and broad rounded snout. Mainly bluish grey with dark mottling. Widespread Indo-Pacific.
Length to 16 cm. Photo: Flores, Indonesia.

Orange-spotted Blenny *Blenniella chrysospilos*

Very shallow reef flats, often surge and high energy zones on outer reefs where occupying the numerous small holes in the reefs. Algae feeders that scrape dead coral bases but quickly retreat to their narrow hide-outs when approached. Readily identified by the red spots that are prominent on the face. Widespread Indo-Pacific. Length to 12 cm. Photo, showing fish out: Toshikazu Kozawa.

Rippled Rockskipper
Istiblennius edentulus

Common in the intertidal zones in protected bays, including mangrove and harbour habitats. Only on high tide seen in a few metres depth. Identified by the regular banded pattern along the body. Widespread Indo-Pacific.
Length to 16 cm, usually about 12 cm.
Photo: Flores, Indonesia.

Thin-lined Rockskipper
Istiblennius lineatus

Intertidal zones, often found in exposed and surge zones where seen hanging onto reef coming out of the water as the level drops from wave action. Scrapes algae of dead corals or rocks. Identified by the thin dark longitudinal lines along the sides. Males have a crest on the head. Widespread Indo-Pacific.
Length to 15 cm.
Photos: Flores, Indonesia.

DRAGONETS - CALLIONYMIDAE

A large, mainly tropical family with 9 genera and about 125 species, but only one commonly observed in the Maldives. Some other species are common in the Maldives, but these live on sandy bottom and are coloured on top accordingly and similar to each other. In all about 10 species can be found here, but apart from rarely being noticed some are almost impossible to identify without collecting specimens. Most species occur in small groups of mixed sexes that are dominated by the largest male. Females usually are considerably smaller than fully grown males. Males usually have extended rays in the dorsal fin or tail, used for display by erecting fins that sometimes bare eye-like spots. Diet comprises small creatures sucked from the sand or rubble with their small but extendable mouth.

Starry Dragonet *Synchiropus stellatus*

Sheltered reefs, along sand and rubble zones with mixed invertebrate and algae growth. Occurs in spread out groups dominated by a large male. Females usually small, looking half the size of the male. In moderate depth in the Maldives, 10 to 40 m. Widespread Indian Ocean, sibling species *S. moyeri* in West Pacific.
Length to 8 cm. Photo of pair shows small male displaying to female, taken by Toshikazu Kozawa.

Tall-fin Dragonet *Synchiropus* sp

Found on outer reef slopes in rubble and sand on the bottom of gutters or other protected areas, usually in the algae zones that are semi-exposed to surge. Well camouflaged species, usually noticed when the male displays to females with the tall dorsal fin. Occurs in small groups and they may bury themselves in sand or fine rubble when not feeding. Undetermined species to about 50 mm long. Photo: Toshikazu Kozawa.

Sand Dragonet *Callionymus* sp

Undetermined, possibly *C. delicatulus*. One of 5 very similar species reported from the Maldives. Mostly found on sand habitats in shallow lagoons and harbours, but one only known from depths over 70 m. Some are tiny, growing a few centimetres long, usually occurring in small groups. Males have tall first dorsal fins that are used for display. Identification is difficult without examining actual specimens.

GOBIES - GOBIIDAE

Gobies are the largest family of marine fishes with an estimated 200 genera and 1500 species worldwide, but comprises various distinctive groups, division is to be expected in the future. They are well represented in the Maldives with about 30 genera and 80 species. The different groups are treated here separately.

SHRIMP GOBIES - GOBIIDAE-1

Some of the most interesting gobies live in a symbiotic relationship with snapping shrimps *Alpheus* spp. The shrimps are responsible for digging burrows and keeping them clean, whilst the goby stands guard at the entrance. The goby signals to the shrimp if safe to come out to dump materials or work at the entrance. Adult gobies are nearly always in pairs but females are often in the burrow and only the male visible. Adult shrimps are usually in pairs as well. Most gobies live with one particular species of shrimp, but as there are many more goby than shrimp species. Shrimps are habitat specific and the various species are distributed over depth and bottom types. They inhabit shallow sandy flats, deep rubble slopes, coarse sand and others prefer fine mud. Gobies feed on small invertebrates, including zooplankton. The number of species in each genus is undetermined at this stage with many taxonomic problems.

Tall-fin Shrimp-Goby *Vanderhorstia prealta*

A spectacular species, usually found in moderately deep water from 20 to 40 m on white sand with fine rubble. It lives with two types of snapping shrimps, *Alpheus randalli* and *A. ochrostriatus*. Readily identified by tall dorsal fin and dark colour. The dorsal fin of the male is considerably taller than that of the female. Only known from Western Indian Ocean. Length to 45 mm. Photo of pair: Neville Coleman. Additional photos: Toshikazu Kozawa.

Twin-spotted Shrimp-Goby
Vanderhorstia ambanoro

Inhabits fine sand or mud habitats, living with grey or brown snapping shrimps. Appears to be rare in the Maldives. Identified by pale colour and series of black spots, male with blue stripes along margin of ventral fin. Shallow to about 20 m depth. Widespread Indo-Pacific. Length to 12 cm.
Photo: John E. Randall.

Blue-barred Shrimp-Goby
Vanderhorstia ornatissima

Commonly found along the edges of shallow seagrass beds and in silty lagoons amongst rubble in a few metres depth. Lives with snapping shrimp species, grey with dark bands on back. Adult fish and shrimp usually occur undeterminedin pairs. Recognised by the thin blue barring or rings near tail along the sides. Widespread Indo-Pacific.
Length to 85 mm.
Photo, upper: Toshikazu Kozawa.

Dracula Shrimp-Goby *Stonogobiops dracula*

Open sand and rubble zones adjacent to reefs in moderate depths, usually in 20+ m, and often seen in pairs. Lives with the red-banded snapping shrimp *Alpheus randalli*. Easily identified by white body and black banded colour pattern. Large individuals develop additional narrow bars between broad ones. Only known from west Indian Ocean. Length to at least 7 cm. Photo, red-banded adult: Jörg Aebi; others: Toshikazu Kozawa.

Fan Shrimp-Goby *Flabelligobius latruncularius*

Open sand and rubble zones adjacent to reefs in moderate depths, usually in 20+ m, and mostly seen solitaire. Lives with the red-banded snapping shrimp *Alpheus randalli*. Identified by slender body with blotched pattern and large first dorsal fin, developing filaments in males. Only known from Red Sea and west Indian Ocean. Length to 10 cm. Photos: Toshikazu Kozawa.

Black Shrimp-Goby
Cryptocentrus fasciatus

Open sand flats and gentle slopes adjacent to reefs from about 10 m depth, often in pairs. Lives with banded snapping shrimps. Mostly black with fine pale spotting or white saddles over top of head and back. Sometimes yellow. Widespread Indo-Pacific. Length to 10 cm.
Photo: Jörg Aebi.

Side-spot Shrimp-Goby
Cryptocentrus strigilliceps

Common in shallow silty lagoons along reef walls and near bommies in the deeper areas to about 10 m depth. Identified by the series of round black spots centrally along the sides, the first spot largest and often edged in white. Lives with grey or dusky snapping shrimps. Widespread Indo-Pacific. Length to 10 cm.

Pink-bar Shrimp-Goby
Amblyeleotris aurora

Common in the Maldives, but usually in depths of about 30 m, occasionally shallower along the bases of outer reefs and lagoon channels on rubble and sand. Lives with the red-banded snapping shrimp *Alpheus randalli*. Widespread Indian Ocean, reported between 10 and 35 m. Length to 11 cm.
Photo: Toshikazu Kozawa.

Diagonal Shrimp-Goby
Amblyeleotris diagonalis

Various protected sand habitats from shallow coarse sand and rubble slope to moderately deep rubble zones along deep reef bases, usually in pairs, living with the blotched snapping shrimp *Alpheus bellulus*. Several similarly banded species, the diagonal stripes on the head are diagnostic for this species. One of the most widespread Indo-Pacific species. Length to 10 cm. Photo: Toshikazu Kozawa.

Broad-banded Shrimp-Goby *Amblyeleotris periophthalma*

Coarse sand and rubble patches on or near reef margins, usually seen singly, living with various grey or brown snapping shrimps, including *Alpheus djiboutensis* that is often yellow. To about 20 m depth. Best identified by the combined spotted and banded patterns. Widespread Indo-Pacific.
Length to 11 cm. Photo, close-up: Toshikazu Kozawa.

Steinitz's Shrimp-Goby *Amblyeleotris steinitzi*

Mainly common in clean white sand lagoons, often in sand patches surrounded by reef where in small spread out groups, to about 10 m depth. Pale in the Maldives and best identified by the occasionally black face and numerous small orange spots in the dorsal fins. Widespread Indo-Pacific, but some geographical variation between Indian Ocean and Pacific. Length to 12 cm. Photos: Toshikazu Kozawa.

Burgundy Shrimp-Goby
Amblyeleotris wheeleri

Shallow reef flats and slopes in rubble, often in gutters or large open patches, including zones with moderate surge, ranging to about 40 m depth. Usually living with the snapping shrimp *Alpheus djiboutensis*. Strongly banded with dark, wine-red. Widespread Indo-Pacific. Length to 10 cm.

Pale Shrimp Goby
Ctenogobiops feroculus

Found commonly on shallow white sand flats in sheltered lagoons and harbours, often in pairs, usually living with the snapping shrimp *Alpheus djiboutensis*. Identified by pale colour and series of black spots and dashes along sides, and black eyes. Widespread Indo-Pacific.
Length to 75 mm.
Photo: Toshikazu Kozawa.

Crocus Shrimp Goby
Ctenogobiops crocineus

Moderately common in clear water lagoons on shallow sand flats with sparse rubble, usually in pairs when adult. Identified by light colour and brown blotches along upper sides and series of orange spots diagonally over head behind eye. Widespread Indo-Pacific.
Length to 7 cm.
Photo: Toshikazu Kozawa.

SAND GOBIES - GOBIIDAE-2

This group includes the gobies that are mainly found resting on the sand and that don't have symbiotic relationships with snapping shrimps. The species are usually similarly coloured and camouflaged with the type of bottom on which they live. They usually lack the bold colours found in reef fishes and are identified by the various spotted or speckled patterns, or by the shape of the head or fins. Food comprises small invertebrates, often filtered from the sand.

Silty Sand-Goby *Gnatholepis cf adjerensis*

A common species in shallow silty lagoons with seagrasses and in harbours with rubble piles on sand. The genus, comprising about 6 species, is characterised by the thin vertical dark line below the eye. This species has small spots all over, including the fins, similar to *G. adjerensis from Indonesia*. Indo-Pacific (?), but several similar species elsewhere and confusion about distribution. At least Indian Ocean, possibly east to Java, Indonesia. Length to 75 mm.

Eye-bar Sand-Goby *Gnatholepis cauerensis*

A common species on mixed rubble, sand and reef habitat, including lagoons and sheltered zones to about 20 m depth. Variable from very pale with few markings to dark with small black spots and some larger white spots over back and along sides, usually to suit habitat. Widespread Indo-Pacific. Often wrongly identified as *G. scapulostigma*, a junior synonym. Length to 65 mm.

Bandit Goby
Gladiogobius ensifer

Moderately common but easily over-looked. Found in sandy lagoons along edges of coral patches with rubble to about 10 m deep. Identified by raised eyes with a horizontal dark band across. Widespread Indo-Pacific.
Length to 75 mm.

Mud-reef Goby
Exyrias belissimus

Silty habitat lagoons, along reef margins and usually below large branching corals that grow on mud and rubble bottoms. Identified by general large size, big head and tall fins. Tail becomes very elongated in large males. Widespread Indo-Pacific.
Length to 15 cm.
Photo: Neville Coleman.

Decorated Sand-Goby
Istigobius decoratus

Found in most sand and rubble habitats. There are several similar species in the Indo-Pacific that are difficult to identifiy, but only one is known so far from the Maldives. It is easily distinguished from other sand gobies by the strongly spotted fins. Other species could be expected. Widespread Indo-Pacific.
Length to 10 cm.

Big-toothed Goby *Macrodontogobius wilburi*

Sand and rubble zones along reef edges in sheltered habitats to about 20 m depth. Identified by combination of series of small but distinctive spots along sides and black marking on cheek. Usually found solitary with other sand gobies and occurs widespread in the Indo-Pacific. Length to 65 mm. Photo: Australia.

Orange-spotted Sand-Goby *Fusigobius* sp 1

Commonly found on rubble reef habitat in the Maldives, but appears to be undescribed and one of an orange spotted species complex, found distributed throughout the Indo-Pacific. Has small but distinctive black or blue spot in first dorsal fin. Probably occurs throughout the west Indian Ocean, but needs to be researched. Length to 50 mm. Photo, juvenile with blue spot: Jörg Aebi.

Inner-spotted Sand-Goby
Fusigobius inframaculatus

Clear sand and rubble reefs habitat or on the sandy patches on the bottom of caves. Shallow to about 15 m depth. Identified by orange spotting and several dark blotches. First dorsal fin with extended ray in adults. Restricted to west Indian Ocean.
Length to 65 mm.
Photo: Jörg Aebi.

Double-spot Sand-Goby *Fusigobius duospilus*

Clear sand and rubble zones among reefs or on the sandy bottom of large overhangs or caves along drop-offs and walls to depths of at least 25 m. Usually in small loose groups. Adults best identified by the double dark spot in the first dorsal fin as shown in the photograph. Widespread Indo-Pacific. Length to 50 mm.

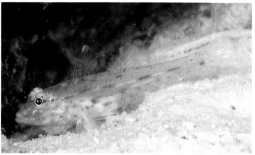

Fine-spotted Sand-goby *Fusigobius neophytus*

Occurs inshore, mainly protected lagoons and harbours. Found on sand and rubble habitats, often silty conditions, to depth of about 10 m. Identified by the mixed pale and dark spotting and usually some short angular lines across the back. Widespread Indo-Pacific. Length to 45 mm.

African Sand-goby *Fusigobius africanus(?)*

Mainly found on reefs on the bottom of sandy caves or below large overhangs on slopes and drop-offs. The heavily pigmented pattern identifies this species. It appears to be synonymous with a species from the east African coast. Length to 45 mm.

Pretty Lagoon-goby
Oplopomus oplopomus

Commonly occurs in silty lagoons and harbours from a few metres depth to very deep mud habitats as in some large lagoons. Deep bodied and ornamented with blue spots. Usually found near large crater-like holes in the mud that were probably made by some invertebrates, and readily dives for cover when approached too closely. Widespread Indo-Pacific.
Length to 10 cm.

Shy Lagoon-goby
Oplopomus caninoides

On sand in current or tidal channels and in moderate depths of 20+ m. More slender than Pretty Lagoon Goby and with larger spotted pattern. A flighty species that swims away, rather than diving into holes. Widespread Indo-Pacific. Length to 65 mm.

Sparsely-spotted Sand-goby
Oplopomops atherinoides

Shallow protected sand habitats in lagoons and harbours. Common in the Maldives. Easily overlooked, as it is well camouflaged on sand and it hugs the bottom closely. Identified by the numerous small brown and white spots all over. Widespread Indo-Pacific. Length to 85 mm.

White Sand-goby
Hazeus maculipinnis

Clear white sand habitat to about 20 m depth. Originally described from the Maldives in 1993 on the basis of a single specimen in the genus *Opua*. It is very plain with only a few dark spots along the side and in the first dorsal fin, eyes and pectoral fins rather large. Length to about 50 mm.
Photo: Toshikazu Kozawa.

REEF GOBIES - GOBIIDAE-3

By far the largest group, but also comprises the smallest species, many of which living secretively in caves and reefs. These are the more colourful gobies and usually have distinctive colouration that identifies the species easily. Many of the small species are new to science and have not yet been named, and more are expected to be discovered, especially in places such as the Maldives where large areas are yet to be explored. Some of the small species are free swimming over corals or in caves, and usually these are planktivores. Others feed on a variety of small invertebrates and also zooplankton.

Yellow Coral-goby *Gobiodon citrinus*

This species lives exclusively in staghorn corals and is often common in lagoons where they form colonies. Like other members in the genus, it has a slimy skin that is toxic. Readily identified by colour and habitat. It is widespread in the Indo-Pacific. Length to 65 mm. Photo, right: Jörg Aebi.

Starry Goby
Asterropteryx semipunctatus

Common in the Maldives in lagoons and protected reef habitats with mixed rubble and silt. Usually found on the bases of large corals amongst rubble with small holes to escape danger, and often in small loose groups to about 10 m depth. Widespread Indo-Pacific. Length to 45 mm.

Full-Moon Reef-goby
Priolepis nocturna

Lives secretively in coral heads on sand. Easily recognised by the white body and black banding. Rare in the Maldives and only known from a few specimens in shallow sandy lagoons to about 10 m depth. Widespread Indo-Pacific, and recently found in Japan at 45 m depth.
Length to 45 mm.
Photo: Jörg Aebi.

Banded Reef-goby
Priolepis cincta

A secretive but common species in reefs, usually observed with a torch when inspecting caves and crevices along reef slopes and walls. Depth range from almost intertidal to at least 50 m. Body distinctly banded and fins yellowish. Widespread Indo-Pacific, ranging into subtropical waters.
Length to 70 mm but usually to 50 mm

Orange-tail Reef-goby
Priolepis inhaca

Sheltered and silty habitats, lagoons and harbours. Secretive in rubble reef where living in pairs. Recognised by the reddish tail and dark edges on the scales. Only known from the west Indian Ocean.
Length to 35 mm.

Yellow-tail Pygmy-goby
Trimma emeryi

Protected reefs, in caves and crevices, usually upside down on ceilings, to about 30 m depth. Similar to *Priolepis* but lacks banding or lines on head. Rather plain in colour, dusky and fins yellowish. West Indian Ocean.
Length to 40 mm.
Photo: Jörg Aebi.

Red-lined Pygmy-goby *Trimma striatum*

Occurs in lagoons and found in small caves or overhangs over sand in coral bommies, usually upside down on the ceilings to about 15 m depth. Easily recognised by the red lines on the face. Widespread Indo-Pacific.
Length to 35 mm.
Photo: Jörg Aebi.

Red Pygmy-goby *Trimma naudei*

Protected reefs, in caves and crevices, usually upside down on ceilings, to about 30 m depth. Identified by the large red blotches almost covering the body. except some white spots variably present on the sides or over back. Widespread Indo-Pacific.
Length to 35 mm.

Orange-spotted Pygmy-goby *Trimma flammeum*

Clear inner reef slopes and walls among rich coral growth mixed with sponges and ascidians, usually resting on latter in wait for zooplankton drifting past. Identified by the close set orange spots over the head and body. Depth range about 10 to 30 m. Widespread west Indian Ocean.
Length to 30 mm.

Red-spotted Pygmy-goby *Trimma* sp 1

Inner reef slopes rich with mixed invertebrates and encrusting algae growth to about 20 m depth. Identified by the red spots over the head and body. Undetermined species that appears to be undescribed.
Length to 30 mm.

Sparsely-spotted Pygmy-goby *Trimma* sp 2

Sheltered rubble and sand slopes with small coral heads or large rubble pieces. Often in silty habitats. Identified by the red spots scattered over head and following part of body. Undetermined species that ranges east to Flores, Indonesia.
Length to 35 mm.
Photo: Jörg Aebi.

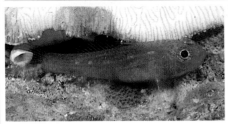

Yellow-spotted Pygmy-goby *Trimma* sp 3

Photographed on the shipwreck "Maldives Victory" at 20 m. Undetermined species, somewhat transparent, showing white spots inside along vertebrate, and yellowish spots over head and body.
Length about 30 mm.

Filamentous Pygmy-goby *Trimma* sp 4

Steep slopes and wall in current prone areas, in caves with rich invertebrate growth and often on the ceiling upside down. Undetermined species, showing little colour but has filamentous first dorsal fin and forked tail.
Length, including long tail, 45 mm.

Sharp-eye Pygmy-goby *Trimma* sp 5

Various coral reef habitats, on bommies in lagoons to outer walls in 6 to 30 m depth. Moderately common and appears to be undescribed. Identified by bright blue in the eye shown in natural light.
Length 25 mm.
Photo: Toshikazu Kozawa.

Taylor's Pygmy-goby *Trimma taylori*

Found in caves along drop-offs and outer reef walls, usually in small groups that are free swimming when feeding on plankton. In depths of 20+ m. A light brownish species with numerous yellow spots and some fins with elongated rays. Widespread Indo-Pacific. Length to 40 mm.

Cave Pygmy-goby *Trimma tevegae*

Found in caves along inner reef drop-offs and outer reef walls, usually in small groups that are free swimming when feeding on plankton. Depth range, 10 to 50 m. Recognised by the broad bluish grey stripe along upper sides and purplish tail. Widespread Indo-Pacific. Length to 35 mm.

White-line Pygmy-goby *Eviota* sp 1

Found commonly on rich coral reef slopes away from strong surge but where moderate tidal currents run. In depths from 6 to 25 m, usually occurring in small groups on large coral heads. Readily identified by the obvious white line through the eye and extending along the body.
Length to 35 mm.

Twin-blotch Pygmy-goby *Eviota* sp 2

Possibly a variation on the White-line Pygmy-goby. Only known from this photograph at this stage.
Length about 25 mm.
Photo: Toshikazu Kozawa.

Sebree's Pygmy-goby *Eviota sebreei*

Clear water reef slopes and walls with rich coral growth. Usually found on rounded coral heads from 6 to 25 m depth. Identified by the series of internal white dashes showing along the back. Widespread and often common throughout the Indo-Pacific. Length to 30 mm.
Photo, centre: Jörg Aebi; right: Toshikazu Kozawa.

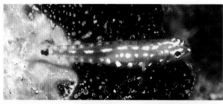

White-spotted Pygmy-goby *Eviota zebrina*

Photographed on inner reef slopes with rich invertebrate growth at about 20 m. Usually in at moderate depths, reported to 40 m. Identified by red to brownish head and body with series of white spots, and black spot at tail fin base. Appears to be rare in the Maldives, reported from few specimens. West Indian Ocean.
Length to 25 mm.
Photo, lower: Jörg Aebi.

Belly-line Pygmy-goby *Eviota sigillata*

Sheltered lagoons on rubble reef zones, usually shallow, to about 10 m depth. Semi-transparent with distinctive black and white lines along head and belly, and a series of short dark lines across the back. Widespread Indo-Pacific.
Length about 20 mm.

Green Pygmy-goby *Eviota guttata*

A common shallow water species in mixed rubble, coral and short algae reef habitats, usually in shallow depths to about 15 m. Identified by the general greenish colour when seen in the wild. West Indian Ocean, with several very similar species elsewhere. Length to about 25 mm.

Red-blotched Pygmy-goby *Eviota melasma(?)*

Sheltered clear water reef habitat. At coral bases and in caves with coralline algae growth. Undetermined species. Many similar species throughout the Indo-Pacific, that are greenish with red spots or blotches.
Length 20 mm.
Photo Jörg Aebi.

Purple-eyed Goby *Bryaninops natans*

Occurs in small groups, usually swimming just above *Acropora* plate corals during slight currents to feed on zooplankton. Well protected coral gardens in lagoons to about 10 m depth. Readily identified by the deep pink to purple eyes. Widespread Indo-Pacific.
Length to 20 mm. Photo: Toshikazu Kozawa.

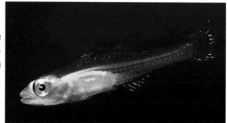

Loki Whip-goby *Bryaninops loki*

This species is moderately common on seawhips and gorgonian corals, but only noticed by those purposely looking for them. Seawhips like current habitats and often stand on coral bommies in tidal channels. Gobies are usually present on the more remote whips. Widespread Indo-Pacific.
Length to 30 mm.

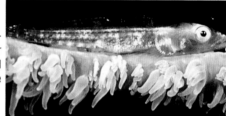

Seawhip Goby *Bryaninops yongei*

Lives mainly on seawhips in the genus *Cirrhipathes* and commonly occur in pairs, and sometimes juveniles are present on the same whip. Eggs are laid on a cleared section and guarded by the parents. Widespread Indo-Pacific.
Length to 40 mm. Photo: Scott Michael.

White-line Whip-goby *Bryaninops amplus*

Lives on *Junceela* seawhips that are in channels of deep lagoons in depths from about 6 m down. Very transparent species with white line and speckles internally along vertebral colomn. Widespread Indo-Pacific.
Length to 40 mm. Photo: Java, Indonesia.

Black-coral Goby *Bryaninops tigris*

Lives on Black Coral bushes, *Anthipathes* sp, growing un rubble ridges or remote patches on sand flats. Usually occurs in groups, sometimes crowding small bushes. Eggs are laid on cleared branches of the coral. Widespread Indo-Pacific.
Length to 40 mm.
Photo, specimen on eggs: Bali, Indonesia.

Slender Sponge-goby *Pleurosicya elongata*

A common species that live on the underside of floppy sponges growing on shallow reef crests and slopes in 3 to 10 m depth. Finding the sponges, usually reveals several of these gobies underneath, and more species are to be expected when looking at differently coloured sponges. Widespread Indo-Pacific. Length to 40 mm.

Cling Goby *Pleurosicya micheli*

Commonly found on corals and sponges on sheltered reef crests and slopes from intertidal to about 30 m depth. Sits openly on the reef. Recognised by the semi-transparent body with a brown stripe from tip of snout to eye, around eye and continuing along sides. Behind eyes lines tapering to a 'V'. Widespread Indo-Pacific.
Length to 30 mm.

Many-host Goby *Pleurosicya mossambica*

Sheltered inner reefs. This species can be found on sponges, ascidians and soft corals. It has red eyes and the body often with some white speckles. Male guards eggs that are laid directly on the host side or near the base. The female may participate or is nearby. Widespread Indo-Pacific.
Length to 26 mm.
Photo, male with eggs: Bali, Indonesia.

SLEEPER GOBIES - GOBIIDAE-4

This groups includes some of the largest gobies in the Maldives. Most species occur in pairs and live on rubble bottom along reef margins. The genus *Valenciennea* makes large homes on sand below solid object, often piling rubble and sand over the area with a small entrance that is covered over at night. They feed by taking a mouth full of sand that is filtered through the gills for tiny creatures. Several similar species that were thought to be just geographical variations appear to be valid species.

Six-spot Sleeper-goby
Valenciennea sexguttata

Sheltered lagoons on white sand, often semi-silty habitat, near reefs or bommies where digging holes under sand covered coral pieces. Adults in pairs, juveniles may form small groups, and rarely deeper than 10 m in the Maldives. Identified by the pale colour, blue spots on the cheek and a small black tip on the dorsal fin. Widespread Indo-Pacific.
Length to 16 cm.

Black-chin Sleeper-goby
Valenciennea cf *puellaris*

Clean white sand slopes, usually in depths of 20+ m. Adults nearly always in pairs, swimming closely together near their hide-outs. Easily recognised by the barred pattern over the back and the black chin. Only known from the west Indian Ocean and was thought to be the same as the spotted Pacific counterpart, *V. puellaris,* or the similar form from Samoa that lacks the black chin. Appears to be undescribed. Length to 20 cm.

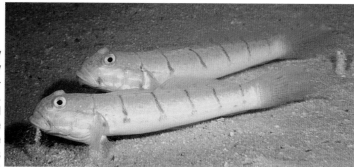

Little Sleeper-goby *Valenciennea parva*

Rare in the Maldives, known from North Malé Atoll. Occurs on sand flats along reef margins and in lagoons with rubble sand, singly or in pairs, to depth of about 15 m. Lacks any distinctive features in the Maldives due to the white sand. Widespread Indo-Pacific. Length to 10 cm. Photo: Flores, Indonesia.

Black-lined Sleeper-goby
Valenciennea helsdingeni

Usually on deep sand flats in the Maldives at 30+ m depth, and open substrate with rubble ridges or near small remote bommies. Readily identified by the two lines running parallel along the body and black blotch in the dorsal fin. Widespread Indo-Pacific. Some variations, lines more black in Pacific populations.
Length to 25 cm in sub-tropical waters, usually 20 cm in the Maldives.
Photo, top: Jörg Aebi.

Golden-head Sleeper-goby
Valenciennea strigata

Clear water reef slopes and crests, often semi-exposed areas, in 6 to 25 m depth. Adults in pairs, juveniles solitary. Easily recognised by the golden-orange head and blue stripe on cheek, but orange variable and occasionally faded to pale yellow. Widespread and common in Indo-Pacific, but less numerous in the Maldives. Length to 18 cm. Photo: Mustag Hussain.

Broad-barred Sleeper-goby
Valenciennea wardii

Usually at moderate depths on fine-sand or mud slopes. Known depth range 10-30 m, but probably much deeper in the Maldives. Readily identified by broad-banded colour pattern. Generally a rare species and included here on two specimens in collections that came from the Maldives. Widespread Indo-Pacific. Length to 15 cm. Photo: Papua New Guinea.

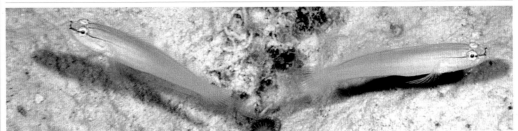

False Sleeper-goby *Amblygobius nocturna*

Lagoons and harbours with fine sand, often silty habitat. Usually in few metres depth, ranging to about 10 m. Adults occur in pairs. Identified by pale colour and stripe from tip of snout running through eye and fading as it goes along the sides of the body. On dark sand it has pink lines but they are faint when on white sand. Widespread Indo-Pacific. Length to 10 cm.

White-barred Reef-goby *Amblygobius semicinctus*

Inshore, seagrass beds and silty lagoons, harbours and reef slopes to about 20 m. Usually very shallow and highly variable in colour with habitat, as shown in the photographs. Widespread Indian Ocean, ranging to Java, Indonesia where it lives sympatric with the very similar Pacific *A. phaleana*. Length to about 10 cm.

Hector's Reef-goby *Amblygobius hectori*

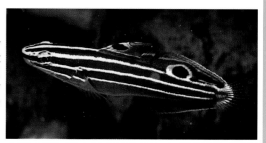

Inner reefs and lagoons with rich coral growth, usually seen single but may occur in pairs or small groups that are loosely distributed in its territory. Readily identified by colour pattern. Widespread Indo-Pacific, but mainly confined to continental regions from the Red Sea to Japan. Length to 65 mm.

DART GOBIES & WORM GOBIES - MICRODESMIDAE

Moderately large family with 12 genera and about 45 species, dividable in two distinct groups presently regarded as subfamilies, MICRODESMINAE, worm gobies and PTERELEOTRINAE, the dart gobies. Previously the latter was included in GOBIIDAE. Worm gobies are usually seen solitary on sand flats and slopes, quickly diving into holes when approached. Dart gobies occur in pairs or small groups. All are planktivores and live in habitats with moderate currents.

Red Fire-goby *Nemateleotris magnifica*

Usually on the bottom of sandy caves along outer reef walls in depths over 15 m. Nearly always found in pairs in the Maldives, but known to form small groups elsewhere. Swims close to the bottom near its burrow, feeding on zooplankton. Readily identified by the white body and dark tail, and tall dorsal fin. Common in the Maldives. Widespread Indo-Pacific.
Length to 75 mm, usually 60 mm.

Purple Fire-goby *Nemateleotris decora*

A deep water species, usually found along deep walls in depths of 40+ m, rarely shallower. Occurs solitary or seen singly, but female shy and often dives into the hole, whilst the male stays out longer and usually noticed. Identified by the dark blue colours seen at depth. Widespread Indo-Pacific.
Length to 75 mm, usually 60 mm.

Arrow Goby *Ptereleotris evides*

Inner and outer reef slopes. Adults usually seen in pairs. Juveniles form small schools in protected inshore habitats around coral heads in shallow depths. Identified by the tall fins, darkened in adults. Adults range to at least 30 m depth. Widespread Indo-Pacific. Length to 10 cm.

Zebra Dart-goby *Ptereleotris zebra*

Found primarily on outer reef slopes in shallow surge zones to about 10 m depth. Often forms large but spread-out schools high above the bottom when food is abundant in currents. A shy species, difficult to approach at close range. Easily identified by the barred pattern along the body. Widespread Indo-Pacific. Length to 12 cm.

Tail-spot Dart-goby *Ptereleotris heteroptera*

Usually found over sand and rubble bottom and often well away from reefs. Occurs in pairs, swim well above the bottom when feeding. In the Maldives rather deep in depths over 20 m, more common in 30 m. Identified by the blue body and black spot in the tail. Widespread Indo-Pacific. Length to 10 cm.

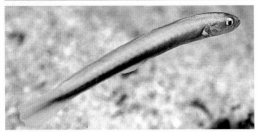

Green-eyed Dart-goby *Ptereleotris microlepis*

Occurs in shallow protected lagoons and harbours. Usually over silty fine sand bottom to about 10 m depth. In pairs or small groups, swimming well above the bottom. No distinctive features, except green eyes. Widespread Indo-Pacific. Length to 12 cm. Photo: Jörg Aebi.

Threadfin Dart-goby *Ptereleotris hanae(?)*

Deep sand flats in 30+ m, seen solitary or in pairs. Swim well above the bottom but readily dives into holes of shrimpgobies when approached too close. Recognised by the filaments on the tail, similar to the Pacific *P. hanae* from Japan but there appears to be a species complex involved with at least one other unde-scribed species in Indonesia. Length to 10 cm.

Weeping Dart-goby *Ptereleotris* sp 1

Undetermined species that appears to be undescribed. It seems closely related to *P. monoptera* that has the black area below the eye, but differs in having a dark area in the caudal fin. Photo: Jörg Aebi.

Splendid Dart-goby
Ptereleotris grammica

The first photo and first record of this beautiful dart-goby from the Maldives. It is readily identified by the colourful markings. In young the mid-lateral line is often black. Usually very deep in 50+ m. Widespread Indo-Pacific. Length to 9 cm. Photo: Jörg Aebi.

Black-spot Worm-goby
Gunnellichthys monostigma

Mainly found on sand crests formed by tidal currents where often in small spread out groups swimming just above the bottom in the flow, staying in the one place. Depth range 1 to 15 m. Body rather plain and best identified by small spot behind the head. Widespread Indo-Pacific. Length to 15 cm.

Neon Worm-goby
Gunnellichthys curiosus

Not common in the Maldives and usually seen in pairs at moderate depths over 20 m, in clear inner reef habitat over rubble zones adjacent to reefs. Swims around in search of food, rather than waiting for plankton drifting past. Identified by the neon blue stripe. Widespread Indo-Pacific.
Length 10 cm.
Photo, upper: Bali, Indonesia; lower: Jörg Aebi.

Orange-line Worm-goby
Gunnellichthys viridescens

Rare in the Maldives, but populations are known to fluctuate greatly elsewhere, being common one year and absent the next. Inshore sand slopes and soft bottom with sparse seagrass and sponge growth in 10 to 30 m depth. Usually seen hovering in current in one place. Identified by orange stripe. Widespread Indo-Pacific.
Length to 12 cm.
Photo: Bali, Indonesia.

MOORISH IDOLS - ZANCLIDAE

Represented by a single widespread species, closely related to surgeonfishes (next family) but lacks spines on the tail and has an almost circular compressed body. The greatly elevated dorsal fin has a long banner like filament.

Moorish Idol *Zanclus cornutus*

Occurs in most reef habitats from shallow flats to deep outer walls. Swims singly, in pairs and occasionally forms schools to either feed or migrate to other areas. Readily identified by shape and colour. Common in the Maldives. Widespread throughout the Indo-Pacific, ranging into subtropical waters. Length to 22 cm.

SURGEONFISHES - ACANTHURIDAE

Large family with 3 subfamilies: ACANTHURINAE, the surgeons, with 4 genera and about 50 species; NASINAE, the unicorns, with a single genus and 15 species; and PRIONURINAE, the sawtails with a few species. The latter is subtropical, although one found in Indonesia, and not represented in the Maldives. 22 surgeonfishes and 8 unicorns are known from the Maldives.

Surgeonfishes feature a sharp blade-like spine in a fold on the tail that points outwards when the tail is bent, and is used for defence or fighting. In some species it is armed with venom. Most species are readily identified by colour and shape, but a few large drab species are similar and may differ in minor, less obvious, detail. Juveniles are similar to adults in shape and colour, only the caudal fin becomes strongly lunate in adults. They occur commonly on reefs where they graze algae of the bottom. Some forms schools or swim in small groups. Juveniles are secretive and often live solitary.

The unicorns have one or two hook-like spines that are external and the sawtails have a series of keeled plates along the tail. Most are herbivores but several combine their diet with all kinds of plankton. Mostly plain coloured fishes, but may tun-on different colour-patterns for display. Some of the large species develop a long, horn- or hump-like, protrusion on the snout when adult, or male. Some species form large schools along outer reef walls.

Blue Tang *Paracanthurus hepatus*

Not common in the Maldives and appears to be localised in only a few areas. Occurs on current-prone reef crests to about 20 m depth. Indian Ocean population differs slightly in colour from Pacific fish when adult, in having white instead of blue along the lower body. The two forms are probably subspecific. Juveniles form small groups and quickly dive for cover in small *Acropora* coral thickets. Widespread Indo-Pacific. Length to 20 cm.

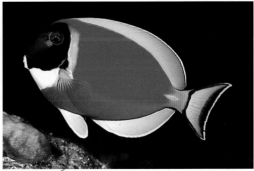

Powder-blue Surgeonfish *Acanthurus leucosternon*

A common and spectacular species that often forms large and dense schools in the Maldives. Readily identified by the black face and blue body. Found in most clear water reef habitats to about 20 m depth. Widespread Indian Ocean, ranging to Bali, Indonesia. Length to 20 cm.

Night Surgeonfish *Acanthurus thompsoni*

Commonly found along outer reef walls, sometimes in schools, feeding well away in open water on plankton. Easily recognised by black body and white tail when in open water. May turn grey when sheltering in reefs or visiting cleaning stations. Occurs at various depths in pursuit of plankton, ranging to at least 50 m depth. Widespread Indo-Pacific. Length to 25 cm.

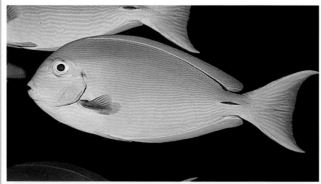

Pale Surgeonfish
Acanthurus mata

A common schooling species in the Maldives, often along inner and outer reef slopes and walls. Sometimes congregating in large caves during the day when currents stop and feed away from the reef when currents are running. Widespread Indo-Pacific.
Length to 45 cm.

Yellow-fin Surgeonfish
Acanthurus xanthopterus

Common in the Maldives, often forming schools in sandy lagoons and show curiosity towards boats and divers. Grazes algae off sand surface and rubble. Occurs in depths from intertidal zones to about 30 m. Identified by the large yellow pectoral fins on the sides. Juveniles have a lined pattern and found inshore in silty habitats. Widespread Indo-Pacific.
Length to 56 cm.

Pencilled Surgeonfish
Acanthurus dussumieri

Adults usually found in moderate depths, rarely seen in less than 25 m. Juveniles often inshore on algae reefs in depths of a few metres but gradually move to deeper water. Identified by white spine and yellow mask over eyes. Protected habitats and adults often seen with shipwrecks. Widespread Indo-Pacific.
Large species, length to 50 cm.

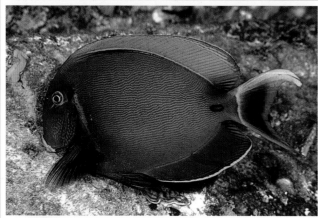

Eye-spot Surgeonfish
Acanthurus bariene

Protected inner reef with large caves or overhands in depths from 15 to 50 m, often seen on shipwrecks. Grazes algae from dead coral or flat surfaces of solid objects. Identified by the distinctive round spot closely behind the eye and yellow-orange dorsal fin. Tail fin with long lobes when adult. Widespread Indo-Pacific.
Length to 40 cm.

Eye-line Surgeonfish
Acanthurus nigricauda

Mainly found on protected inner reefs, grazing algae on shallow crests and slopes. Identified by the dark stripe behind the eye and over the tail spine. Variable grey to almost black all over and often shows a white band on the tail. Widespread Indo-Pacific.
Length to 45 cm.
Photo: Bali, Indonesia.

Lieutenant Surgeonfish
Acanthurus tennenti

Various reef flats and slopes from silty inshore to outer reefs, often in small groups, to about 15 m depth. Identified by the double stripe behind the head at eye level and blue line around tail spine in adults. Widespread Indian Ocean, ranging east to Bali, Indonesia. Length to 30 cm.

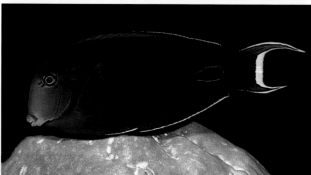

Ring-tail Surgeonfish
Acanthurus auranticavus

Shallow protected reef flats and slopes to outer reef walls. Often in small groups and mixes with other similar species. Often almost black with only a white band around the tail. Other features, such as orange around spine, not always visible. Widespread Indo-Pacific.
Length to 45 cm.
Photo: Bali, Indonesia.

White-spine Surgeonfish *Acanthurus leucocheilus*

Shallow protected reef flats and slopes to outer reef walls, to about 20 m depth. Singly or in small groups. Large adults almost black but spine distinctly white, sometimes white band around tail, and juveniles have a white tail as well. Widespread Indo-Pacific.
Length to 45 cm. Photo right, adult,: Neville Coleman; juvenile with white tail: Bali, Indonesia.

Spot-face Surgeonfish *Acanthurus maculiceps*

Rare in the Maldives and only seen once on outer reef slopes in about 10 m depth where several swam together on a shipwreck. Mainly west Pacific, Maldives represents the western known limit of range. Easily identified by the numerous yellow spots over the entire head. Length to 40 cm. Photo, closeup: Bali, Indonesia

Lined Surgeonfish
Acanthurus lineatus

Shallow reef flats and slopes that are usually exposed to surge and currents to about 10 m depth. Forms schools in gutters when adult. Small juveniles secretive among boulder rubble. Easily identified by lined patterns. Tail spine is venomous in this species. Widespread Indo-Pacific. Length to 35 cm.

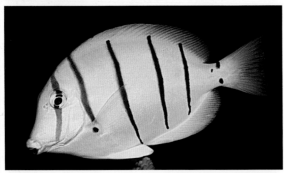

Convict Surgeonfish
Acanthurus triostegus

Shallow protected lagoons and commonly found around jetties. Often forms large schools where freshwater runs over reef, grazing on the rich algae growth in such areas. Easily identified by pale body with vertical black stripes. Widespread Indo-Pacific. Length to 20 cm.

White-spotted Surgeonfish
Acanthurus guttatus

Found schooling in very shallow depths, usually between 1 and 5 m, inshore on reefs. Mainly surge zones, where often seen near the breaking waves in water filled with small air-bubbles. The white spotting on the body is thought to represent the air-bubbles for camouflage. Widespread Indo-Pacific. Length to 26 cm. Photo: Roger Steene, Christmas Island.

Mimic Surgeonfish
Acanthurus tristis

Clear reef slopes and crests. Appears to be localised in the Maldives, seen commonly in some places. Adults whitish on the head and around eye, followed by black over pectoral fin base. Juveniles mimic small angelfishes such as *Centropyge eibli.* Has non-mimic form in the Maldives that is yellow with orange speckles but could have additional mimic forms, yet to be discovered. Ranges east to Bali, Indonesia.
Length to 20 cm.
Photos, top, adult and juvenile: Bali, Indonesia.

Dusky Surgeonfish
Acanthurus nigrofuscus

Clear inner to outer reef slopes in channels and gutters. Grazes algae from rubble and dead coral bases, but also feeds on plankton at times. Identified by the black spots near the tail fin base and the tail fin that looks purple or blue in natural light. Widespread Indo-Pacific.
Length to 20 cm.

Fine-lined Bristletooth *Ctenochaetus striatus*

Forms schools in lagoons along reef slopes with large rubble zones, such as smashed staghorn corals from storms, that have good algae cover. They graze in groups and prefer soft algae that grow on rubble as well as on sand. Identified by the numerous thin horizontal lines and spotting around the eye. Widespread Indo-Pacific.
Length to 25 cm.

Two-spot Bristletooth
Ctenochaetus binotatus

Protected reef slopes with rich invertebrate growth such as large soft corals and where encrusting algae covers rubble and coral bases. Identified by the brown body with numerous thin pale lines, spots on the face and two dark spots above and below the tail fin base. Juveniles have a bright yellow tail fin. Widespread Indo-Pacific.
Length to 18 cm.
Photo: Neville Coleman

Gold-ring Bristletooth *Ctenochaetus strigosus*

Clear inner reef crests and slopes. Usually seen singly or in small loose groups in reef gutters. Identified by the numerous small pale dots all over and yellow around the eye. Small juveniles sometimes all yellow with blue eye. Widespread Indo-Pacific. Length to 18 cm.

Sailfin Surgeonfish
Zebrasoma desjardinii

Protected inner reefs and in large lagoons. Adults usually seen in pairs along rubble zones at shallow depths to about 25 m. Juveniles inshore, solitary, and seek protection among staghorn corals. Widespread Indian Ocean, ranging to Java, Indonesia. Replaced by sibling species *Z. veliferum* in the West Pacific east from Java.
Length to 40 cm.

Brown Tang *Zebrasoma scopas*

Protected shallow reefs, often forming schools when feeding on slopes with good algae growth among the corals. Small juveniles secretive in staghorn corals. Identified by dark colour, rounded body and white spine. Sometimes bright yellow, xanthic phase, one such individual seen in the Maldives by the author. Widespread Indo-Pacific. Length to 20 cm.

Yellow-tail Tang
Zebrasoma xanthurum

Rare in the Maldives, those seen are possible strays from the mainland. Larval stages can be pelagic for a long time. Reported from North Malé Atoll. Mainly known from the Red Sea and Arabian Gulf where they form large schools in 2 to 20 m depth. Readily identified by the blue body and bright yellow tail.
Length to 25 cm.
Aquarium photo.

Orange-spine Unicornfish
Naso lituratus

Shallow inner and outer reef crests and slopes, occasionally seen in deep water. Adults usually in pairs, sometimes forming schools in the Maldives. Identified by the bright orange spines on the tail. Widespread Indo-Pacific, but two forms divided between Indian Ocean and Pacific. Both forms occur together in Bali, Indonesia, suggesting they are separate species.
Length to 45 cm.
Photo, lower, Indian Ocean form in Bali, showing scars from a fight. The Pacific form that has a mostly black dorsal fin is more common there and most-likely inflicted the wound.

Big-nose Unicornfish
Naso vlamingii

Commonly occurs on clear water reefs along upper regions of deep drop-offs. Often seen in loose groups feeding on plankton well away from reefs in currents. Males often display with intensified blue colours that can quickly change and may go very pale all over when visiting cleaning stations. Widespread Indo-Pacific.
Length to 55 cm.
Photo, lower, dark form: Neville Coleman.

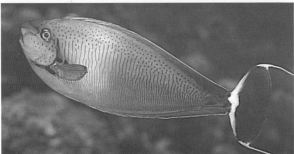

Spotted Unicornfish
Naso brevirostris

Very common in the Maldives on inner to outer reefs along upper parts of slopes and drop-offs. Forms schools in pursuit of plankton at various depths, including on the surface where their horns can be seen protruding above the surface. Males can quickly change colour, showing a broad bluish white band to impress other members of the species. Widespread Indo-Pacific.
Length to 50 cm.

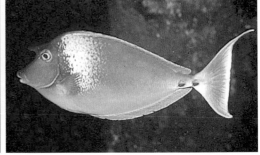

Blue-spine Unicornfish *Naso unicornis*

Protected shallow reef habitat with good algae growth. Adults usually near moderately deep water and seen to about 40 m depth. Juveniles inshore in algae rich reefs. Feeds on the bottom or loose floating weeds. Identified by the blue spines, juveniles lack the horny protrusion on the head. Widespread Indo-Pacific.
Length to 70 cm. Photo right , dark form, Bali: Indonesia.

Humpback Unicornfish
Naso brachycentron

Usually seen on outer reef slopes or along deep walls where forming moderately large schools. Identified by the light grey colour and camel-like hump on the back. In addition, males have a thin protruding spine in front of the eyes. Widespread Indo-Pacific. Length to 70 cm.
Photo, upper: male, and female below.

Hump-nose Unicornfish
Naso tuberosus

Mainly seen along outer reef walls in shallow depths, singular or in small groups. Young inshore on algae rich reefs. Males have an hump on their back and develop a large rounded snout, extended well in front of the mouth. Feeds on algae and plankton. Widespread Indo-Pacific. Length to 60 cm.
Photo upper, male: Australia.

Sleek Unicornfish
Naso hexacanthus

Common in the Maldives along drop-offs where they feed in schools on plankton. Great depth-range, reported from 135 m. Identified by the blue tail and is also known as the Blue-tail Unicorn. Widespread Indo-Pacific. Length to 75 cm, usually 50 cm. Adult above, juvenile below. Photo, juvenile: Jörg Aebi.

One-spine Unicornfish
Naso thynnoides

Inner and outer reef slopes, forming large schools at times. They travel along at a steady pace near the reef edge in pursuit of plankton. A small species that is identified by the thin vertical lines along the back and the single spine on the tail, compared to two in similar species. Widespread Indo-Pacific. Length to 40 cm.

RABBITFISHES - SIGANIDAE

A tropical Indo-Pacific family with a single genus, comprising about 30 species, and at least 5 of which occur in the Maldives. Dividable into two subgenera, but the long-snouted species, subgenus *Lo*, not in the Maldives. This family has some unusual features: a spine at both ends of the ventral fins, with 3 rays in between; and 7 spines in the anal fin (3 or less in most similar fishes). All fin spines are venomous and a stab causes agonising pain. Most species occur in pairs in the Maldives and usually associate with algae-rich reefs. One species schools. Seagrass beds need to be investigated for other species as more than half of all the species associate with seagrasses and potentially could occur in the Maldives. A species seen in seagrass beds is probably *Siganus margaritiferus*, requiring verification. All feed on algae, weeds and seagrasses.

Starry Rabbitfish
Siganus stellatus

Large adults usually seen in pairs along reef edges bordering onto sand and rubble in lagoons in inner reefs. Usually shallow but ranges to about 35 m depth near outer reefs where filamentous algae grow at moderate depths. Identified by the numerous close set dark spots all over. Widespread Indian Ocean, ranging to Java, Indonesia. Red Sea form is sub-specific and has yellow tail.
Length to 40 cm.

Schooling Rabbitfish
Siganus argenteus(?)

Sheltered inner reef slopes with rich algae growth. Usually seen in pairs in the Maldives and appears to be different from the Indonesian schooling populations that have a forked tail and larger yellow spots. Most similar to an undescribed species from Japan and perhaps the same. Possibly two species in the Maldives. *S. argenteus* is reported widespread Indo-Pacific.
Length to 30 cm.
Photo, lower: *S. argenteus*, schooling: Flores, Indonesia.

Coral Rabbitfish
Siganus corallinus

Usually seen in pairs in rich coral reef slopes. Two yellow species in the Maldives. This species is deep-bodied and has black area on the throat. Widespread Indian Ocean, ranging to Java, replaced by *S. tetrazona* further east, easily distinguised by lack of black on the throat.
Length to 35 cm.

Chin-strap Rabbitfish
Siganus puelloides

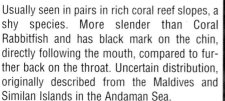

Usually seen in pairs in rich coral reef slopes, a shy species. More slender than Coral Rabbitfish and has black mark on the chin, directly following the mouth, compared to further back on the throat. Uncertain distribution, originally described from the Maldives and Similan Islands in the Andaman Sea.
Length to 35 cm.
Photo: Roger Steene.

Sri Lankan Rabbitfish *Siganus* sp

Rare in the Maldives. A common coastal species in Sri Lanka and near Indian coast. Recognised by the strong pattern of longitudinal lines along entire body. Replaced by similar *S. guttatus* with spots instead of lines in Indonesia and a sibling species *S. lineatus* further east from eastern Australia to southern Japan. Length to about 25 cm.
Photo: John E. Randall, Sri Lanka.

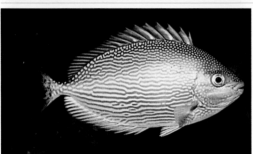

Java Rabbitfish *Siganus javus*

Mainly coastal habitas, estuaries and lagoons. A common mainland species, not often seen in the Maldives. Easily recognised by the white spotting or lines and large black area in caudal fin. Widespread Indo-Pacific. Lenth to 40 cm.
Photo: Java, Indonesia.

TUNAS & MACKERELS - SCOMBRIDAE

A large commercially important family with 15 genera and nearly 50 species worldwide. The large tunas are oceanic and occasionally seen along outer reef walls. They are targeted commercially, forming the basis of the worlds largest fishing industry. Few species visit reefs. Most family members are streamlined fast fishes that hunt other fishes and pelagic invertebrates such as squid.

Dogtooth Tuna
Gymnosarda unicolor

A common species along deep outer reef walls, usually singly but occasionally several together. Often shows curiosity towards divers and makes a close pass. Feeds on other small pelagic fishes and reef planktivores venturing too far out. Widespread Indo-Pacific. Length to about 2 m.

Mouth Mackerel *Rastrelliger kanagurta*

Not common in the Maldives. It occurs in moderate to large schools along deep slopes and drop-offs to feed on zooplankton, but may target eggs of spawning fishes at specific times. Easily recognised when feeding by the large expanded mouth and silvery reflective gills. Widespread Indo-Pacific. Length to about 35 cm.

LEFT-EYED FLOUNDERS - BOTHIDAE

Very large family with 15 genera and 90 species distributed in the Indo-Pacific, and double that worldwide. Poorly represented away from continental waters, and only few recorded from the Maldives. No doubt more will turn up as many species have pelagic larvae that can travel long distances. These fishes have adapted to laying on their sides on the bottom. Both eyes are on one side (upperside) that faces upwards and is pigmented like the surroundings for camouflage, whilst the other (underside) is blind and often unpigmented. There are several other families that are closely related, but not yet known from the Maldives. The various families are either left or right-eyed, meaning that the eyes are on that particular side. They feed on various bottom creatures, including various invertebrates, worms and fishes.

Leopard Flounder
Bothus pantherinus

Clear water reef sand flats from shallow areas near reefs or deep open flats close to remote bommies with fine rubble patches. Identified by numerous pale flower-shaped spots all over upper sides and eyes highly elevated. Males with long filaments on upper pectoral fin that are used for display. Widespread Indo-Pacific.
Length to 30 cm.

RIGHT-EYED FLOUNDERS - PLEURONECTIDAE

A large and very diverse family with 45 genera and about 100 species. Comprises several sub-genera and only SAMARINAE is represented with a single species. It is one of the smallest species, amongst generally large fishes that are commercially harvested in many sub-tropical regions. They feed on a variety of invertebrates and fishes.

Three-eyed Flounder
Samariscus triocellatus

Clear water inner reef slopes to outer reef walls, in sandy bottoms of large caves or below reef overhangs. Buries during the day and becomes active on dusk. Moves around like a slug but waving its upper pectoral fin. Identified by small size, slender shape and series of dark blotches centrally along back. Widespread Indo-Pacific.
Length to 10 cm.
Photo: Charles Anderson.

SOLES - SOLEIDAE

Large family, mostly small fishes, with 30 genera and over 100 species. Only recently one member found in the Maldives. Generally prefer coastal and often muddy habitats. Both eyes are on right-hand side. During the day they are usually buried in the sand. Some have strong banded or spotted patterns on the pigmented sides, and some juveniles are brightly coloured, mimicking nudibranchs or flatworms.

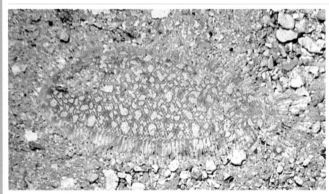

Pebble Sole
Pardachirus sp

Members of this genus are usually found on sand along reef margins, usually where sand is mixed with slightly courses reef particles. This species was recently photographed in a shallow lagoon at Ari Atoll. Appears to be undescribed.
Length to 20 cm.
Photo: Charles Anderson.

FILEFISHES - MONACANTHIDAE

Large family with about 30 genera and over 100 species, of which 8 genera and at least 11 species occur in the Maldives. Many more species occur in nearby continental waters and as they can have a long pelagic stage, more can be expected in the Maldives. More than half of all the species occur in Australian waters. Similar to triggerfishes, but generally more compressed, often thin bodies and dorsal fin with a prominent separate single spine, often armed with downward series of spines on the sides. Maldives species associate with reefs and can be found in protected inner reefs and lagoons. Diet comprises various invertebrates and algae, but the larger species are also scavengers.

Long-nose Filefish
Oxymonacanthus longirostris

Also called Harlequin Filefish. Clear inner reef crests with rich coral growth, usually in *Acropora* thickets feeding on coral polyps. Juveniles forming small groups and adults usually seen in pairs. Readily identified by shape and orange spotted colour pattern. Widespread Indo-Pacific.
Length to 10 cm.

Mimic Filefish
Paraluteres prionurus

Sheltered reef habitats in mixed soft coral and algae, often deep in the Maldives along slopes at the bases of drop-offs of inner reef between 20 to 40 m. Mimic of *Canthigaster* pufferfishes (see Fig. 5., page 16), mainly *valentini*, but some geographical variations. Maldives populations with strong reticulated pattern in the white areas, and mimic not as convincing as in Pacific. Likely to take on different forms where other *Canthigaster* pufferfishes occur. Widespread Indo-Pacific.
Length to 10 cm.

Ear-spot Filefish
Pervagor janthinosoma

Various reef areas with rich coral and other invertebrate growth that provide good cover, on crests to about 20 m depth. Usually seen in the shade of overhanging corals, sometimes making a quick dash over short open spaces. Territorial, occasionally seen fighting. Best recognised by the greenish colour and vertical blotch at gill opening. Common in the Maldives. Widespread Indo-Pacific.
Length to 13 cm. Photo: Bali, Indonesia.

Orange Filefish
Pervagor aspricaudus

Secretive on inner reef slopes, mainly semi-silty habitats with mixed soft coral, sponges, and algae reefs. Not often seen in the Maldives, and usually when a torch is used to check darker areas in reefs. Looks pale orange with numerous small spots in natural light. Sporadic occurrence in Indo-Pacific.
Length to 13 cm

Rhino Filefish
Pseudaluteres nasicornis

Usually on sand slopes with ridges of rubble with soft corals and seawhips. Often lines up vertically with seawhips and hide behind. Adults in pairs and usually in depths in excess of 15 m. Rare in the Maldives. Widespread Indo-Pacific, ranging to subtropical zones. Length to 18 cm.
Photo: Bali, Indonesia.

Scribbled Leatherjacket
Aluteres scriptus

Juveniles pelagic to about 10 cm long, swimming with floating weeds or sheltering in large jellies, and settle inshore in sheltered often muddy habitat. Adults move to deep water and swim along slopes and drop-offs, usually in 20+ m depth. Best identified by very large tail fin. Widespread in all tropical seas.
Longest filefish, when including extremely long tail in large individuals, reaching 1 m.

Broom Filefish
Amanses scopas

Clear water reef crest with mixed coral rubble and sand patches, semi-protected areas with shelter in gutters and coral coverage to hide. Rather shy in the Maldives, adults in pairs. Identified by dark colour and brush-like patch of spines on sides of male. Widespread Indo-Pacific.
Length to 20 cm.
Photo: Sulawesi, Indonesia.

Barred Filefish
Cantherhinus dumerilii

Clear water inner reef slopes with good coral growth, adults usually seen in pairs. Identified by size and colour, males have yellow spines on sides of tail fin base. Very shy species in the Maldives, quickly swimming out of sight or diving for cover under large corals. Small juveniles spotted. Widespread Indo-Pacific. Length to 35 cm.
Photo: Sulawesi, Indonesia.

Spectacled Filefish
Cantherhinus fronticinctus

Protected inner and outer reef habitats, adults usually in depths of 20+ m. Juveniles inshore and sometimes under jetties among large algae on pylons or with sponges. Secretive and often camouflaged. Identified by white band around tail base and dark stripes along body. Widespread Indo-Pacific.
Length to 23 cm.
Photo: Bali, Indonesia.

Honeycomb Filefish *Cantherhinus pardalis*

Various reef habitats with rich algae and sargassum weed growth, including shallow outer reef zones exposed to surge. Juveniles often in floating weeds until reaching reefs to settle. Variable in colour and best identified by white saddle spot on top of the tail fin base. Widespread Indo-Pacific.
Length to 25 cm. Photo, right: Java, Indonesia.

TRIGGERFISHES - BALISTIDAE

Moderately large family with 12 genera and over 40 species in tropical waters worldwide, of which 10 genera and 17 species reported from the Maldives. Big-headed fishes with eyes placed high and well back. Dorsal fin features a strong spine that can be locked in upright position by second smaller spine. The spine is used at night when sleeping in crevices, the triggerfish wedging itself in crevices so it can't be pulled out be a predator. Mouth is small but the strong jaws feature dog-like teeth that are used to crush hard-shelled snails or other invertebrates. Some large species favour urchins and have learned to manipulate them, biting spines away until the inside part can be attacked and consumed. Few species form large schools to feed on zooplankton.

Starry Triggerfish
Abalistes stellatus

Occurs mainly on moderately deep slopes and occasionally comes inshore, and often in silty habitat. Adults often seen swimming high above the bottom over open substrate. Small juveniles are found in the same areas, but hide on solid matter, especially dead coral pieces or bits of wood with small holes. Widespread Indo-Pacific.
Length to 25 cm.
Photo: Flores, Indonesia.

Striped Triggerfish
Balistapus undulatus

Common in various reef habitats, in the Maldives from sheltered shallow lagoons to outer reefs to at least 50 m depth. Readily identified by greenish colour and yellow to orange lines. Males lack stripes over top of snout. Widespread Indo-Pacific. Length to 30 cm.

Clown Triggerfish *Balistoides conspicillum*

Adults swim openly about, usually seen along steep slopes or walls, and retreating to caves when approached but sometimes unafraid of divers. Juveniles secretive in small caves with rich invertebrate growth, often deep, usually in excess of 30 m. Readily identified by colours. Widespread Indo-Pacific. Length to 35 cm. Photo, juvenile: Jörg Aebi.

Titan Triggerfish *Balistoides viridescens*

The largest triggerfish, also known as Giant Triggerfish. Sheltered inner reef slopes adjacent to moderately deep water. Often aggressive towards divers, especially when caring for eggs, but may attack unprovoked by charging at great speed. A hit with their solid jaws with or without biting, either way, wow it hurts! Widespread Indo-Pacific. Length to 75 cm. Photo: Neville Coleman.

Yellow-margin Triggerfish
Pseudobalistes flavimarginatus

Inshore species, adults often on shallow seagrass beds and juveniles usually with remote bommies on open sandy bottoms in silty habitats, sometimes in small groups. Large males congregate in loose groups over sand flats away from reefs to prepare nesting sites. Adults identified by the short horizontal stripes behind the eye and juveniles by the numerous black spots. Widespread Indo-Pacific.
Length to 60 cm.

Yellow-spotted Triggerfish
Pseudobalistes fuscus

Juveniles (above) typically occur solitary with small remote coral bommies on sand, in clear-water channels in depths of about 15 to 40 m. Adults generally deep and usually seen when spawning on deep sand flats adjacent to reefs in 30+ m depth. Widespread Indo-Pacific.
Length to 55 cm, including pointed part of caudal fin, but excluding the filamentous parts .

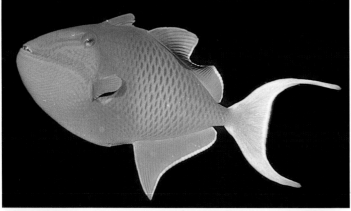

Blue Triggerfish
Odonus niger

Occurs in schools in current channels in entrances to lagoons and along reef walls. They feed on zooplankton in currents, often in massive schools that fill the entire water column. Easily recognised by the generally blue colour when adult. Widespread Indo-Pacific, but different forms between Indian and Pacific Oceans. Indian Ocean form has longer stripe from the mouth that goes along entire head, compared to short in Pacific form. Length to 40 cm, including long caudal fin lobes.

Picasso Triggerfish
Rhinecanthus aculeatus

Hawaiian Triggerfish. Shallow protected lagoons and harbours, often in silty habitat around rubble pieces or small bommies. Dig their own shelter under solid objects by swimming sand away: meaning that they put their mouth on a solid part and swim like crazy to create current that takes the sand with it. Identified by the long snout and colour pattern. Widespread Indo-Pacific. Length to 25 cm.

Wedge-tail Triggerfish
Rhinecanthus rectangulus

Not common in the Maldives and mainly confined to shallow reef slopes exposed to surge on outer reefs. Sometimes seen openly swimming about, but a shy species that quickly runs for cover. Readily identified by long snout and black markings. Widespread Indo-Pacific. Length to 25 cm.

Strickland's Triggerfish
Rhinecanthus cinereus

Little is known about this species and appears to prefer clear outer reef conditions. The few specimens reported were at moderate depths, ranging to 25 m. Appears to be widespread Indian Ocean, but rare and only known from a few oceanic locations, including Mauritius and Andaman Sea.
Length to 25 cm.
Photo: Jörg Aebi.

Bridled Triggerfish *Sufflamen freanatus*

In the Maldives moderately common on deep open sand flats with remote low reef patches and rubble at 30+ m depth. Identified by plain brown to yellowish colour all over, male with stripe along snout. Juveniles dark over back and side pale with thin lines. Widespread Indo-Pacific. Length to 35 cm.

239

Boomerang Triggerfish
Sufflamen bursa

Clear inner reefs and outer reef habitats with mixed invertebrate and algae habitat from surge zones to 90 m depth. Identified by pale colour and boomerang-shaped stripe over head, passing through back of eye. Widespread Indo-Pacific.
Length to 30 cm.

Half-moon Triggerfish
Sufflamen chrysopterus

Inner reef crests and slopes and semi-exposed outer reef habitats with rubble and sand patches or borders of reef to about 35 m depth. Adults with distinctive tail fin pattern ending in a part-moon shaped white margin. Small juveniles yellow on top and white from below eye level separated by black stripe. Widespread Indo-Pacific.
Length to 30 cm.

Black Triggerfish
Melichthys niger

Inner and outer reef slopes, mainly in upper areas adjacent to deep water. In loose groups in which males dominate females in separate territories. Sometimes high above reefs when feeding on plankton. Looks almost black underwater with white along the bases of the dorsal and anal fins. Tail lacks white and becomes lunate in large individuals. Widespread Indo-Pacific. Length to 30 cm.

Indian Triggerfish
Melichthys indicus

Mainly on inner reef crests and slopes with mixed rich coral growth and rubble patches, to about 20 m depth. Digs holes below coral bases for shelter. Identified by general black colour and white lines at dorsal and anal fin bases Distinguished from the similar Black Triggerfish by the rounded tail that has a white edge. Widespread Indian Ocean, ranging to Java, Indonesia.
Length to 24 cm.

Gilded Triggerfish
Xanthichthys auromarginatus

Occurs in moderate depths along outer reef walls, usually in 35+ m, where loose groups of mixed sexes gather in current areas to feed on zooplankton. Identified by shape and colour: females grey with series of small white spots along scale rows; male with additional orange fin margins and blue area from mouth to below eye. Widespread Indo-Pacific.
Length to 22 cm.

Blue-line Triggerfish
Xanthichthys caeruleolineatus

Occurs deep along outer reefs. Mainly known from depths over 100 m. May rise to shallower depth when feeding on zoo-plankton. Identified by mid-lateral blue line from behind the pectoral fin. Both sexes are similar, males with lines on cheek. Widespread Indo-Pacific.
Length to 30 cm.
Photo: Jörg Aebi.

Oceanic Triggerfish
Canthidermis maculatus

Adults usually only seen when coming to deep sand flats to spawn. Mostly oceanic, juveniles below floating weeds or objects and adults school in open oceanic waters. Adults flighty and identified by greyish overall colour and large size. Widespread Indo-Pacific.
Length to 50 cm.

BOXFISHES - OSTRACIIDAE

Tropical family with 6 genera and 20 species, only one genera and two species commonly seen in the Maldives. Two other genera reported from trawls or the stomachs of pelagic predators, and may occur in deep water only. Boxfishes have a hard external skin made of fused scales that encloses much of the body with holes for the movable parts: tail, fins, mouth, eyes and gills. In some species (not yet known from the Maldives) there are horn-like protrusions in front of the eyes or on the back. The skin or mucus may have poison that is released under stress. It can cause casualties when collecting aquarium fishes. They should be kept completely separate and water regularly replaced when first caught, as the poison will kill the boxfish itself. Food comprises various invertebrates but most species favour worms from sandy bottoms.

Yellow Boxfish
Ostracion cubicus

A common species on most reef habitats but changes habitat with growth. Large adults are mostly found on deep slopes and drop-offs on protected reefs to at least 40 m depth. Juveniles often in shallow protected bays or harbours in holes and under ledges with urchins. Easily identified by the square yellow body and black spots when small. More elongate when adult. Widespread Indo-Pacific. Length to 45 cm.
Photo above, small juvenile: Toshikazu Kozawa.

Black Boxfish *Ostracion meleagris*

Prefers clear water reefs with good coral cover on slopes and shallow drop-offs. Males recognised by the yellow spots and blue sides often swims openly about, but the black with many small white spots patterned female is more secretive in the reefs. Usually in depths less than 20 m. Widespread Indo-Pacific. Length to 20 cm.

PUFFERFISHES - TETRAODONTIDAE

Large family with about 20 genera and over 100 species, of which 5 genera and 18 species have been recorded from the Maldives. Dividable into subfamilies with the short-snouted TETRAODON-TINAE, usually growing large, and long-snouted CANTHIGASTERINAE, that are mostly small. Pufferfishes are named for their ability to inflate themselves into balloon-like shapes. Any predator trying to eat them finds that it got more than it bargained for. In some cases this has killed a predator who couldn't let go, but killing both predators and prey. In addition, the skin and flesh is poisonous that can be fatal to humans if consumed. They are mostly bottom fishes that either live on reefs or on sand flats. Larvae are pelagic and few species are completely pelagic. Food comprises a great variety of invertebrates, algae, and some are scavengers.

Saddled Pufferfish *Canthigaster valentini*

Adults usually swim openly on reefs in pairs, juveniles solitary and often shy in reefs. One of the best known small pufferfishes that is often noticed on reefs because of the distinctive colour pattern. It serves as a warning to predators "I'm poisonous", and there are a number of look-alikes that are not poisonous at all. The best example is the Mimic Filefish *Paraluteres prionurus* that will fool anybody that is not aware of it. Only the long transparent fins compared to the short paddle-like ones of the pufferfish will tell them apart (see Fig. 5., page 16). Sometimes the filefish swims near the pufferfish. Widespread Indo-Pacific. Length to 10 cm.

Crowned Pufferfish *Canthigaster coronata*

Usually on deep sand flats and slopes with patches or ridges with rich invertebrate growth such as seawhips and sponges. In the Maldives mostly in depths of 25+ m. Very similar to saddled pufferfish but saddles short. Maldives fish very pale, probably because of white sand, compared to Pacific fish that feature orange margins along black saddles and ornamented with blue. Widespread Indo-Pacific, Indian Ocean and Pacific populations slightly different and both forms occur in Bali, Indonesia. Length to 14 cm.

Smith's Pufferfish *Canthigaster smithae*

Clear inner reef habitat, often on slopes along bases of drop-offs or steep slopes, with mixed rubble and boulders in depths of about 30 m. Usually seen solitary. Identified by dark top and white belly. West Indian Ocean only. Length to 13 cm.

Tyler's Pufferfish *Canthigaster tyleri*

Clear water inner and outer reef walls, usually in large caves, swimming with belly towards vertical sides and often upside-down on ceilings. Adults usually in loose pairs. Identified by pale side with close set dark spots and scribbles on snout and over top of head. Widespread Indian Ocean, replaced by *C. leoparda* in Pacific. Length to 85 mm. Photo right: Jörg Aebi.

Ambon Pufferfish *Canthigaster amboinensis*

Inner and outer reefs from shallow surge zones to about 15 m depth. Secretive in small dark caves and crevices, a flighty species. Identified by the light-blue spots over the body, whitish when juvenile, and lines radiating upward from behind the eyes. Widespread Indo-Pacific.
Length to 12 cm. Photo: Bali, Indonesia.

False-eye Pufferfish *Canthigaster papua*

Shallow protected lagoons, harbours, and reef flats with rubble and sand mix. Adults commonly in pairs. Variable in colour with habitat, best identified by numerous small bluish white spots and a ring-like mark on the back at the base of the fin. Widespread Indo-Pacific. Length to 9 cm.

White-spotted Pufferfish *Canthigaster janthinoptera*

Inner and outer reefs from shallow surge zones to at least 40 m depth, rich coral algae mix habitat. Secretive in small caves and crevices or intertwining branching sponges. Identified by the white spots over the body that increase in size below, and male develops short greenish lines radiating from the eyes. Widespread Indo-Pacific. Length to 8 cm.

Bennett's Pufferfish *Canthigaster bennetti*

Inshore, often silty habitats, algae reefs, harbours and protected weedy lagoons to about 30 m depth. Adults usually in pairs. Variable in colour with habitat, finely spotted and a dark elongated spot on back at base of fin. Widespread Indo-Pacific. Length to 9 cm.

Scribbled Pufferfish *Arothron mappa*

Various clear water reef habitats with rich invertebrate growth. Often in caves during the day and adults mainly active at night. Highly variable in colour and spotting, sometimes with numerous thin black lines. Usually short black lines radiating from the eyes, except very large individuals that have lines encircling the eyes. Widespread Indo-Pacific. Length to 60 cm.

245

Guineafowl Pufferfish
Arothron meleagris

Protected inner reef habitats, usually at moderate depths but often seen shallow in the Maldives on reef crest in 6 m or just down along top of drop-offs and slopes. Identified by the numerous white spots all over, but sometimes has bright yellow phase that maybe completely yellow or with black blotches. Latter often confused with *A. nigropunctatus* but the black blotches feature the tiny white spots. Sometimes found in pairs of different colour forms. Widespread Indo-Pacific.
Length to 45 cm.
Photo, yellow form: Roger Steene, Christmas Island, Indian Ocean.

Black-spotted Pufferfish
Arothron nigropunctatus

Inner and outer reef slopes and crests with rich invertebrate growth and algae mix, often found with sponges, to depth of about 30 m. Highly variable in colour from grey to yellow-orange with few to many black spots, sometimes all yellow. Widespread Indo-Pacific.
Length to 30 cm.
Photo, yellow form: Neville Coleman.

Yellow-eye Pufferfish
Arothron immaculatus

Mud and sand habitat, usually sleeping during the day in low depressions or partly buried. Active at night, feeding on invertebrates like sand-urchins. Identified by plain grey to brown colour, yellow eye and yellow to dark blotch around pectoral fin base. Widespread Indian Ocean, ranging to Australia and Indonesia, replaced by lined sibling *A. manilensis* in Pacific. Length to 30 cm.

Stars-and-Stripes Pufferfish
Arothron hispidus

Sheltered inshore habitats, coastal bays and deep open sand stretches between reefs with sparse growth, often semi-silty habitats. Highly variable grey to near black with white spots over back and lines along belly, and a black area around pectoral fin base. Widespread Indo-Pacific. Length to 50 cm. Photo: Australia.

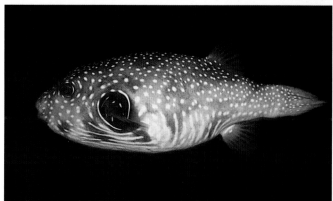

Starry Pufferfish
Arothron stellatus

Juveniles inshore in silty habitats, often estuarine, adults on deep slopes around inner and outer reefs, sometimes swimming in surface waters. Highly variable, changing with growth from a fine zebra-lined pattern when a small juvenile, to small dark spots all over when adult. Widespread Indo-Pacific.
Large species, length to 1 m.
Photo, lower right, large juvenile: Mabul, Malaysia: small juvenile below: Flores, Indonesia.

PORCUPINEFISHES - DIODONTIDAE

Small family with 6 or 7 genera and about 20 species worldwide, 3 of which genera and 4 species reported from the Maldives. None are common and single individuals are usually sighted. Like the closely related pufferfishes, they quickly inflate themselves in defence when handled. The spines that normally lay flat, stand-up and project outwards so the whole fish becomes a prickly ball. Most species are active at night and shelter in caves during the day, usually at moderate depths. However, in the Maldives some large individuals can be seen hovering in the shallows above reefs at times during the day, for no apparent reason. Diet comprises various hard-shelled invertebrates, but sometimes includes jellies.

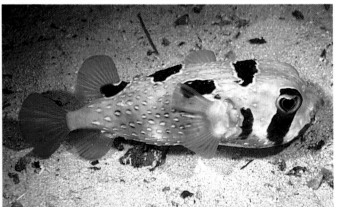

Blotched Porcupinefish
Diodon liturosus

Hides during the day in crevices or below overhanging reef, in moderately deep inshore reefs to about 40 m depth. Active at night, entering shallow sand flats, feeding on hard-shelled invertebrates. Identified by the large black blotches. Widespread Indo-Pacific.
Length to 45 cm.
Photo, juvenile: Bali, Indonesia.

Black-spotted Porcupinefish
Diodon hystrix

Usually in deep coastal reefs, in caves during the day, but occasionally adults are seen swimming above reef in surface waters, where shy. Juveniles pelagic to moderate sizes and drift with weed rafts or other floating matter. Recognised by the numerous black spots over back and sides. Occurs widespread in all tropical seas.
Length to 70 cm.
Photo: Flores, Indonesia.

Few-spined Porcupinefish *Chilomycteris reticulatus* ✓ ♂ baby.

Deep coastal slopes, adults usually in depths of 20+ m, mainly entering shallow depths at night. Juveniles pelagic to about 20 cm length and drift with floating weeds or objects. Has few spines on the body and fins with numerous small black spots. Widespread in all tropical seas, ranging into subtropical waters. Length to 55 cm. Photo: Bali, Indonesia.

Rounded Porcupinefish
Cyclichthys orbicularis

Clear protected reefs, on slopes with sponge and algal habitats. Often in large sponges during the day, active at night and feeding among reefs on invertebrates. Mainly brownish, lacking any black spots or blotches. Widespread Indo-Pacific. Small species, length to 20 cm.
Photos: Bali, Indonesia.

INDEX TO FAMILIES AND SPECIES

Abalistes **235**
  stellatus **235**
Ablabys **59**
  binotatus **60**
  macracanthus **59**
Abudefduf **149**
  notatus **149**
  septemfasciatus **149**
  sexfasciatus **150**
  sordidus **150**
  vaigiensis **149**
ACANTHURIDAE *218*
Acanthurus **219**
  auranticavus **221**
  bariene **220**
  dussumieri **220**
  guttatus **222**
  leucocheilus **221**
  leucosternon **219**
  lineatus **222**
  maculiceps **222**
  mata **220**
  nigricauda **221**
  nigrofuscus **223**
  tennenti **221**
  thompsoni **219**
  triostegus **222**
  tristis **223**
  xanthopterus **220**
Aethaloperca **67**
  rogaa **67**
Aluteres **234**
  scriptus **234**
Amanses **234**
  scopas **234**
Amblycirrhites **138**
  bimaculata **138**
Amblyeleotris **200**
  diagonalis **201**
  periophthalma **201**
  steinitzi **201**
  wheeleri **201**
Amblyglyphidodon **150**
  batunai **150**
  leucogaster **150**
Amblygobius **215**
  hectori **215**
  nocturna **214**
  semicinctus **214**
Amblypomacentrus **147**
  sp 1 **147**
Amphiprion **140**
  clarkii **141**
  nigripes **140**
  sebae **141**
Anampses **165**
  caeruleopunctatus **165**
  lineatus **165**
  meleagrides **165**
  twistii **166**
Anemonefish **140**
  Blackfoot **140**
  Clark's **141**
  Yellow-tail **141**
ANEMONEFISHES **140**
Angelfish **130**
  Blue-face **132**
  Blue-ringed **133**
  Coral Beauty **134**
  Damsel **134**

(Angelfish)
  Eibl's **134**
  Emperor **132**
  Half-circled **132**
  Hybrid **131**
  Indian Cherup **134**
  Lyre-tail **135**
  Many-spined **133**
  Moonbeam **133**
  Regal **130**
  Smoke **131**
  Three-spot **131**
ANGELFISHES *130*
Anglerfish **36**
  Clown **36**
  Freckled **37**
  Giant **36**
  Painted **37**
  Sargassum **37**
  Spotfin **37**
ANGLERFISHES *36*
ANOMALOPIDAE *40*
ANTENNARIIDAE *36*
Antennarius **36**
  coccineus **37**
  commersoni **36**
  maculatus **36**
  nummifer **37**
  pictus **37**
Anyperodon **72**
  leucogrammicus **72**
Aphareus **111**
  furca **111**
Apogon **82**
  angustatus **82**
  apogonides **83**
  cf bandanensis **85**
  cf fuscus **85**
  cf savayensis **84**
  doryssa **86**
  evermanni **85**
  exostigma **84**
  freanatus **84**
  gilberti **86**
  holotaenia **82**
  kallopterus **83**
  leptacanthus **86**
  nigrofasciatus **82**
  sangiensis **86**
  sp 1 **83**
  sp 2 **83**
  sp 3 **85**
  sp 4 **85**
  taeniophorus **82**
APOGONIDAE *80*
Apolemichthys **131**
  trimaculatus **131**
  xanthurus **131**
  xanthurus x trimaculatus **131**
Aprion **111**
  virescens **111**
APSILININAE *106*
Archamia **88**
  fucata **88**
Arothron **245**
  hispidus **247**
  immaculatus **247**
  mappa **245**
  meleagris **246**
  nigropunctatus **246**

(Arothron)
  stellatus **247**
Aspidontus **192**
  dussumieri **192**
  taeniatus **192**
Asterropteryx **207**
  semipunctatus **207**
ATHERINIDAE *32*
Atherinomorus **32**
  lacunosus **32**
AULOSTOMIDAE *48*
Aulostomus **48**
  chinensis **48**
Balistapus **236**
  undulatus **236**
BALISTIDAE *235*
Balistoides **236**
  conspicillum **236**
  viridescens **237**
Bannerfish **128**
  Masked **129**
  Phantom **128**
  Reef **128**
  Schooling **129**
  Singular **129**
Barracuda **153**
  Great **153**
BARRACUDAS *153*
Basslet **62**
  Flame **75**
  Orange **76**
  Pink **75**
  Red **74**
  Reef **62**
  Resplendent **76**
  Short-snout **76**
  Threadfin **73**
  Two-spot **74**
  Yellow-back **73**
  Yellow-eye **74**
  Yellow-tail **75**
BASSLETS *61, 73*
Batfish **97, 135**
  Boer's **136**
  Silver **97**
  Tall-fin **136**
BATFISHES *135*
BELONIDAE *34*
Belonoperca **62**
  chabanaudi **62**
Bigeye **79**
  Blotched **80**
  Crescent-tail **79**
BIGEYES *79*
Black Jack **93**
Blanquillo **89**
  Blue **89**
  Flagtail **89**
Blenniella **196**
  chrysospilos **196**
BLENNIES *191*
  REEF **193**
  SABRETOOTH **191**
BLENNIIDAE *191*
BLENNIIDAE-1 **191**
BLENNIIDAE-2 **193**
Blenny **191**
  Bearded Sabretooth **193**
  Big-nose **196**
  Black-eared Eyelash **193**

(Blenny)
  Chestnut Eyelash **194**
  Crested Sabretooth **193**
  False Cleanerfish **192**
  Imposter **191**
  Jewelled **196**
  Lance **192**
  Leopard **195**
  Lined Combtooth **195**
  Little Combtooth **194**
  Lyre-tail Combtooth **195**
  Mimic **191**
  Orange-spotted **196**
  Red-streaked Eyelash **194**
  Smith's Venomous **191**
  Tube-worm **192**
  Two-colour Combtooth **194**
Blue Tang **219**
Bodianus **178**
  anthioides **179**
  axillaris **178**
  bilunulatus **179**
  bimaculatus **179**
  diana **178**
Bolbometopon **181**
  muricatum **181**
BOTHIDAE *231*
Bothus **231**
  pantherinus **231**
Boxfish **242**
  Black **242**
  Yellow **242**
BOXFISHES *242*
Brachysomophis **29**
  crocodilinus **29**
Bream **99**
  Large-eye **103**
  Monocle **99**
Bristletooth **223**
  Fine-lined **223**
  Gold-ring **224**
  Two-spot **224**
Brotula **35**
  multibarbata **35**
Bryaninops **211**
  amplus **211**
  loki **211**
  natans **211**
  tigris **211**
  yongei **211**
Bullseye **119**
BULLSEYES *119*
Butterflyfish **121**
  Black Pyramid **121**
  Black-back **123**
  Blackened **125**
  Brown **123**
  Chevroned **122**
  Citron **123**
  Double-saddle **124**
  Eclipse **121**
  Head-band **125**
  Indian **127**
  Lined **124**
  Long-nose **128**
  Madagascar **127**
  Meyer's **126**
  Ornate **126**
  Pig-face **124**
  Pinstriped **122**

(Butterflyfish)
Pyramid *121*
Racoon *122*
Spotted *123*
Teardrop *121*
Threadfin *124*
Triangular *125*
Vagabond *125*
Very-long-nose *128*
Yellow *122*
Yellow Teardrop *121*
Yellow-head *126*
BUTTERFLYFISHES *121*
Caesio *112*
caerulaurea *112*
lunaris *112*
teres *113*
varilineata *112*
xanthonota *113*
CAESIONIDAE *112*
Callechelys *30*
marmorata *30*
CALLIONYMIDAE *197*
Callionymus *198*
sp *198*
Calloplesiops *77*
altivelis *77*
Calotomus *187*
carolinus *187*
spinidens *187*
Cantherhinus *234*
dumerilii *234*
fronticinctus *234*
pardalis *235*
Canthidermis *241*
maculatus *241*
Canthigaster *243*
amboinensis *244*
bennetti *245*
coronata *243*
janthinoptera *245*
papua *244*
smithae *244*
tyleri *244*
valentini *243*
CARANGIDAE *92*
Carangoides *93*
caeruleopinnatus *93*
ferdau *93*
fulvoguttatus *94*
orthogrammus *94*
plagiotaenia *94*
Caranx *92*
ignobilis *92*
lugubris *93*
melampygus *93*
sexfasciatus *92*
Cardinalfish *81*
Arrow-tooth *81*
Barred *85*
Big-eye *84*
Black-striped *82*
Black-tail *88*
Cave *85*
Clear-finned *85*
Copper-striped *82*
Cross-eyed *87*
Elat *87*
Five-line *81*
Gilbert's *86*
Grey-ring *85*
Harbour *87*

(Cardinalfish)
Long-spine *86*
Maldives *83*
Narrow-striped *82*
Night *86*
Nose-spot *88*
Painted *88*
Pearly-lined *82*
Peppered *87*
Plain *83*
Sangi *86*
Short-striped *83*
Slender *88*
Spiny-eye *84*
Spiny-head *83*
Spotless *84*
Tail-spot *89*
Tiger *81*
Toothy *81*
Variegated *87*
Yellow-edged *85*
CARDINALFISHES *80*
Catfish *35*
Striped *35*
CATFISHES *35*
Centropyge *133*
acanthops *134*
bispinosa *134*
eibli *134*
flavicauda *134*
flavipectoralis *133*
multispinis *133*
Cephalopholis *64*
argus *65*
boenak *65*
leoparda *66*
miniata *64*
nigripinnis *66*
polleni *66*
sonnerati *65*
spiloparaea *65*
Cetoscarus *180*
bicolor *180*
Chaetodon *121*
auriga *124*
baronessa *125*
bennetti *121*
cf plebeius *122*
citrinellus *123*
collare *125*
decussatus *125*
ephippium *126*
falcula *124*
guttatissimus *123*
interruptus *121*
kleinii *123*
lineolatus *124*
lunula *122*
lunulatus *122*
madagaskariensis *127*
melannotus *123*
meyeri *126*
mitratus *127*
ornatissimus *126*
oxycephalus *124*
plebeius *122*
triangulum *125*
trifascialis *122*
trifasciatus *122*
ulietensis *124*
vagabundus *125*
xanthocephalus *126*

CHAETODONTIDAE *121*
Cheilinus *174*
chlorourus *175*
fasciatus *174*
oxycephalus *175*
trilobatus *174*
undulatus *175*
Cheilio *157*
inermis *157*
Cheilodipterus *81*
artus *81*
isostigma *81*
macrodon *81*
quinquelineatus *81*
Chilomycteris *249*
reticulatus *249*
Chlidichthys *77*
inornatus *77*
Choeroichthys *52*
brachysoma *52*
Chromis *142*
atripectoralis *142*
delta *144*
dimidiata *143*
elerae *144*
flavipectoralis *143*
lepidolepis *144*
nigroanalis *145*
nigrura *145*
opercularis *144*
pembae *143*
ternatensis *143*
viridis *142*
weberi *144*
xutha *143*
Chrysiptera *147*
biocellata *147*
brownriggii *147*
glauca *148*
unimaculata *148*
Cirrhilabrus *171*
exquisitus *171*
rubrisquamis *171*
Cirrhitichthys *137*
aprinus *138*
falco *137*
oxycephalus *137*
CIRRHITIDAE *137*
Cirrhitus *139*
pinnulatus *139*
Cirripectes *193*
auritus *193*
castaneus *194*
stigmaticus *194*
Cleaner Wrasse *167*
Blue-streak *167*
Two-colour *167*
CLEANER WRASSES *166*
Cleanerfish, false *192*
CLUPEIDAE *32*
Cod *64*
Rock *64*
Combtooth Blenny *194*
Lined *195*
Little *194*
Lyre-tail *195*
Two-colour *194*
Comet *77*
CONGRIDAE *31*
Coral Beauty *134*
Coral Grouper *63*
Black-saddle *64*

(Coral Grouper)
Indian *63*
Squaretail *63*
Coral-goby *206*
Coris *155*
batuensis *155*
cuvieri *156*
frerei *156*
Corythoichtys *51*
flavofasciatus *51*
haematopterus *51*
insularis *51*
schultzi *51*
Crenimugil *154*
crenilabis *154*
Crescent Perch *78*
Cryptocentrus *200*
fasciatus *200*
strigilliceps *200*
Ctenochaetus *223*
binotatus *224*
striatus *223*
strigosus *224*
Ctenogobiops *202*
crocineus *202*
feroculus *202*
Cyclichthys *249*
orbicularis *249*
Cymolutes *158*
praetextatus *158*
Cyprinocirrhites *138*
polyactis *138*
DACTYLOPTERIDAE *54*
Dactylopus *54*
orientalis *54*
Damsel *141*
Azure *145*
Blue-yellow *145*
Fusilier *148*
Indian *146*
Jewel *151*
Johnston's *151*
Lyretail *147*
Narrowbar *151*
One-spot *148*
Pale-blue *148*
Philippine *146*
Regal *147*
Scribbled *146*
Sharp-eye *152*
Surge *147*
White-band *152*
White-saddled *147*
White-tail *146*
DAMSELFISHES *140*
DAMSELS *145*
FARMER *151*
DART GOBIES *215*
Dart-goby *217*
Arrow *216*
Green-eyed *216*
Splendid *217*
Tail-spot *216*
Threadfin *216*
Weeping *216*
Zebra *216*
Dascyllus *141*
aruanus *141*
carneus *142*
trimaculatus *142*
Decapterus *96*
macarellus *96*

Dendrochirus **56**
  biocellatus **56**
  brachypterus **56**
  zebra **56**
Diagramma **104**
  sp 1 **104**
Diodon **248**
  hystrix **248**
  liturosus **248**
DIODONTIDAE *248*
Diploprion **62**
  bifasciatum **62**
Dipterygonotus **115**
  balteatus **115**
Dogtooth Tuna **230**
Doryrhamphus **52**
  bicarinatus **53**
  exicus **53**
Dottyback **77**
  Pink-head **77**
  Yellow **77**
DOTTYBACKS *77*
Dragonet **197**
  Sand **198**
  Starry **197**
  Tall-fin **197**
DRAGONETS *197*
Dragonfish **48**
  Little **48**
Dunckerocampus **52**
  multiannulatus **52**
ECHENEIDAE *91*
Echeneis **91**
  naucrates **91**
Echidna **27**
  nebulosa **27**
  polyzona **27**
Ecsenius **194**
  bicolor **194**
  lineatus **195**
  midas **195**
  minutus **194**
Eel **28**
  Black-pitted **29**
  Crocodile **29**
  Garden **31**
  Napoleon **29**
  Ribbon **28**
  Snake **30**
  Spaghetti **31**
EELS *29*
  GARDEN **31**
  MORAY **29**
  SNAKE **29**
  WORM **29**
EELTAIL CATFISHES *35*
Elagatis **95**
  bipinnulata **95**
Emperor **100**
  Black-blotch **101**
  Blue-line Large-eye **102**
  Blue-spotted Large-eye **102**
  Gold-spot **103**
  Large-eye **103**
  Long-nose **101**
  Orange-finned **100**
  Orange-stripe **100**
  Red-spot **102**
  Small-tooth **101**
  Spangled **101**
  Yellow-lip **100**
EMPERORS *100*

Entomacrodus **196**
  striatus **196**
EPHIPPIDAE *135*
Epibulus **174**
  insidiator **174**
Epinephelus **68**
  areolatus **70**
  caeruleopunctatus **69**
  fasciatus **72**
  flavocaeruleus **72**
  fuscoguttatus **71**
  lanceolatus **71**
  longispinis **70**
  macrospilos **69**
  melanostigma **68**
  merra **69**
  ongus **69**
  polyphekadion **70**
  spilotoceps **68**
  tauvina **68**
  undulosus **71**
ETELININAE *106*
Eurypegasus **48**
  draconis **48**
Eviota **209**
  guttata **210**
  melasma(?) **210**
  sebreei **210**
  sigillata **210**
  sp 1 **209**
  sp 2 **209**
  zebrina **210**
Exallias **195**
  brevis **195**
Exyrias **203**
  belissimus **203**
Eyelash Blenny **193**
  Black-eared **193**
  Chestnut **194**
  Red-streaked **194**
Filefish **232**
  Barred **234**
  Broom **234**
  Ear-spot **233**
  Honeycomb **235**
  Long-nose **232**
  Mimic **233**
  Orange **233**
  Rhino **233**
  Spectacled **234**
FILEFISHES *232*
Fire-goby **215**
  Purple **215**
  Red **215**
Fistularia **49**
  commersonii **49**
FISTULARIIDAE *49*
Flabelligobius **200**
  latruncularius **200**
Flagtail **79**
FLAGTAILS *79*
Flashlight Fish **40**
  Red Sea **40**
FLASHLIGHT FISHES *40*
Flathead **60**
FLATHEADS *60*
Flounder **231**
  Leopard **231**
  Three-eyed **231**
FLOUNDERS *231*
  LEFT-EYED **231**
  RIGHT-EYED **231**

Flutemouth **49**
  Smooth **49**
FLUTEMOUTHS *49*
FLYING GURNARDS *54*
Foa **87**
  abocellata **87**
  fo **87**
Forcipiger **128**
  flavissimus **128**
  longirostris **128**
Fowleria **87**
  aurita **87**
  punctulata **87**
  variegata **87**
Fusigobius **204**
  africanus(?) **205**
  duospilus **204**
  inframaculatus **204**
  neophytus **205**
  sp 1 **204**
Fusilier **112**
  Banana **114**
  Blue-dash **114**
  Broad-stripe **114**
  Dwarf **115**
  Gold-band **112**
  Moon **112**
  Slender **115**
  Striped **114**
  Thin-lined **112**
  Yellow-back **113**
  Yellow-banded **113**
  Yellow-stripe **113**
  Yellow-tail **113**
Fusilier Snapper **111**
FUSILIERS *112*
Garden Eel **31**
  Splendid **31**
  Spotted **31**
Genicanthus **135**
  caudovittatus **135**
GERREIDAE *97*
Gerres **97**
  abbreviatus **98**
  acinaces **98**
  oblongus **97**
  oyena **98**
Ghostpipefish **49**
  Coralline **50**
  Ornate **49**
  Robust **50**
GHOSTPIPEFISHES *49*
Gladiogobius **203**
  ensifer **203**
Glass-eye **79**
Gnathanodon **94**
  speciosus **94**
Gnathodentex **103**
  aurolineatus **103**
Gnatholepis **202**
  cauerensis **203**
  cf adjerensis **202**
Goatfish **115**
  Bar-tail **118**
  Dash-and-Dot **116**
  Double-bar **117**
  Long-barbel **116**
  Round-spot **116**
  Schooling **118**
  Shiny **118**
  Square-spot **117**
  Yellow-saddle **115**

(Goatfish)
  Yellow-spot **117**
  Yellow-stripe **117**
GOATFISHES *115*
GOBIES *198*
  DART **215**
  REEF **206**
  SAND **202**
  SLEEPER **212**
  WORM **215**
GOBIIDAE *198*
  GOBIIDAE-1 **198**
  GOBIIDAE-2 **202**
  GOBIIDAE-3 **206**
  GOBIIDAE-4 **212**
Gobiodon **206**
  citrinus **206**
Goby **199**
  Arrow **216**
  Bandit **203**
  Big-toothed **204**
  Black-coral **211**
  Cling **212**
  Coral **206**
  Dart **216**
  Fire **215**
  Lagoon **205**
  Many-host **212**
  Mud-reef **203**
  Purple-eyed **211**
  Seawhip **211**
  Shrimp **199**
  Sleeper **213**
  Sponge **211**
  Starry **207**
  Whip **211**
Gomphosus **168**
  caeruleus **168**
Gorgasia **31**
  maculata **31**
  preclara **31**
Gracila **67**
  albomarginata **67**
Grammistes **61**
  sexlineatus **61**
Gregory **152**
  Blunt-snout **153**
  Dusky **153**
  Indian **152**
  White-banded **152**
Grouper **63**
  Black-spot **68**
  Blacktip **72**
  Coral **63**
  Flower **71**
  Foursaddle **68**
  Giant **71**
  Greasy **68**
  Honeycomb **69**
  Long-spined **70**
  Lunar-tailed **67**
  Red-flushed **67**
  Small-spotted **69**
  Snout-spots **70**
  Snubnose **69**
  Squaretail **70**
  Wavy-lined **71**
  White-edged **68**
  White-lined **72**
  White-speckled **69**
  White-square **67**
  Yellow-fin **72**

GROUPERS *61, 63*
Grubfish *188*
  Black-tail *188*
  Lyre-tail *189*
  Maldivian *188*
  Thousand-spot *188*
GRUBFISHES *188*
GRUNTERS *78*
Gunnellichthys *217*
  curiosus *217*
  monostigma *217*
  viridescens *217*
Gurnard *54*
  Flying *54*
Gymnocaesio *115*
  gymnoptera *115*
Gymnocranium *102*
  grandoculis *102*
  microdon *102*
  sp *103*
Gymnomuraena *27*
  zebra *27*
Gymnosarda *230*
  unicolor *230*
Gymnothorax *24*
  berndti *27*
  breedeni *24*
  favagineus *24*
  fimbriatus *26*
  flavimarginatus *25*
  javanicus *25*
  meleagris *25*
  nudivomer *25*
  richardsoni *26*
  sp. *25*
  undulatus *26*
  zonipectis *26*
HAEMULIDAE *104*
Halfbeak *33*
  Dussumier's *33*
  Reef *33*
HALFBEAKS *33*
Halichoeres *161*
  cosmetus *161*
  hortulanus *163*
  leucoxanthus *161*
  marginatus *162*
  nebulosus *162*
  scapularis *162*
  trispilus *161*
  vrolikii *162*
  zeylonicus *163*
Hardyhead *32*
  Robust *32*
  Silver *32*
HARDYHEADS *32*
Hawkfish *137*
  Blotched *138*
  Coral *137*
  Forster's *139*
  Longnose *137*
  Lyre-tail *138*
  Ring-eye *138*
  Spotted *137*
  Two-spot *138*
  White-spotted *139*
HAWKFISHES *137*
Hazeus *206*
  maculipinnis *206*
Helcogramma *190*
  maldivensis *190*
  sp *190*

Hemigymnus *177*
  fasciatus *177*
  melapterus *177*
HEMIRAMPHIDAE *33*
Hemitaurichthys *121*
  zoster *121*
Heniochus *128*
  acuminatus *128*
  diphreutes *129*
  monoceros *129*
  pleurotaenia *128*
  singularius *129*
Herklotsichthys *32*
  quadrimaculatus *32*
Herring *32*
  Gold-spot *32*
HERRINGS *32*
Heteroconger *31*
  hassi *31*
Heteropriacanthus *80*
  cruentatus *80*
Hippocampus *53*
  hystrix *53*
  kuda *53*
Hipposcarus *181*
  harid *181*
Histrio *37*
  histrio *37*
Hogfish *178*
  Coral *178*
  Diana *178*
  Lyre-tail *179*
  Red-lined *179*
  Saddle-back *179*
  Yellow *179*
HOGFISHES *178*
HOLOCENTRIDAE *41*
HOLOCENTRIDAE-1 *41*
HOLOCENTRIDAE-2 *45*
HOLOCENTRINAE *41*
Hologymnosus *157*
  annulatus *157*
  doliatus *157*
Hoplolatilus *90*
  cuniculus *90*
  sp 1 *90*
  sp 2 *90*
Humbug *141*
  Damsel *141*
  Indian *142*
  Three-spot *142*
HUMBUGS *141*
Hypoatherina *32*
  barnesi *32*
Hyporhamphus *33*
  affinis *33*
  dussumieri *33*
Idol *218*
  Moorish *218*
Istiblennius *196*
  lineatus *197*
Istigobius *203*
  decoratus *203*
JACKS *92*
Jobfish *111*
  Green *111*
  Small-tooth *111*
Kuhlia *79*
  mugil *79*
KUHLIIDAE *79*
KYPHOSIDAE *120*
Kyphosus *120*

(Kyphosus)
  cinerascens *120*
  vaigiensis *120*
Labrichthys *168*
  unilineatus *168*
LABRIDAE *155*
LABRIDAE-1 *155*
LABRIDAE-2 *160*
LABRIDAE-3 *166*
LABRIDAE-4 *168*
LABRIDAE-5 *171*
LABRIDAE-6 *173*
LABRIDAE-7 *173*
LABRIDAE-8 *178*
Labrobsis *167*
  xanthonota *167*
Labroides *167*
  bicolor *167*
  dimidiatus *167*
Lagoon-goby *205*
  Pretty *205*
  Shy *205*
Large-eye Bream *103*
Large-eye Emperor *102*
  Blue-line *102*
  Blue-spotted *102*
Leaf-Fish *59*
  Indian *60*
  Spiny *59*
Leatherjacket *234*
  Scribbled *234*
Leopard Wrasse *160*
  Ornate *160*
  Splendid *160*
Lepidozygus *148*
  tapeinosoma *148*
Leptojulis *163*
  cyanopleura *163*
Leptoscarus *187*
  vaigiensis *187*
LETHRINIDAE *100*
Lethrinus *100*
  erythracanthus *100*
  harak *101*
  lentjan *102*
  microdon *101*
  nebulosus *101*
  obsoletus *100*
  olivaceus *101*
  xanthochilus *100*
LINGS *35*
Lionfish *55*
  Common *55*
  Dwarf *56*
  Spotfin *55*
  Two-eyed *56*
  White-lined *55*
  Zebra *56*
LIONFISHES *54, 55*
Liopropoma *62*
  africanum *62*
  susumi *62*
Lizardfish *38*
  Grey-streak *39*
  Indian *38*
  Nose-spots *39*
  Painted *40*
  Red-marbled *40*
  Tail-blotch *39*
  Variegated *39*
LIZARDFISHES *38*
LOBOTIDAE *78*

Lobotus *78*
  surinamensis *78*
LONGFINS *77*
LUTJANIDAE *106*
Lutjanus *106*
  argentimaculatus *108*
  bengalensis *106*
  biguttatus *109*
  bohar *109*
  erenberghi *107*
  fulvus *108*
  gibbus *108*
  kasmira *106*
  madras *107*
  monostigma *107*
  rufolineatus *107*
  sebae *109*
Lyretail *68*
  White-edged *68*
Mackerel *230*
  Mouth *230*
MACKERELS *230*
Macolor *110*
  macularis *110*
  niger *110*
Macrodontogobius *204*
  wilburi *204*
Macropharyngodon *160*
  bipartitus *160*
  ornatus *160*
MALACANTHIDAE *89*
Malacanthus *89*
  brevirostris *89*
  latovittatus *89*
Mangrove Jack *108*
Maori Wrasse *174*
  Banded *174*
  Cheek-line *176*
  Little *177*
  Oriental *176*
  Point-head *175*
  Thin-line *176*
  Triple-tail *174*
  White-dotted *175*
Meiacanthus *191*
  smithi *191*
Melichthys *240*
  indicus *240*
  niger *240*
MICRODESMIDAE *216*
MONACANTHIDAE *232*
Monocle Bream *99*
MONODACTYLIDAE *97*
Monodactylus *97*
  argenteus *97*
Monotaxis *103*
  grandoculis *103*
MOORISH IDOLS *218*
Moray *24*
  Albino *25*
  Bar-tail *26*
  Barred *27*
  Black Cheek *24*
  Clouded *27*
  Giant *25*
  Honeycomb *24*
  Little *26*
  Peppered *28*
  Undulate *26*
  White-eyed *28*
  White-mouth *25*
  Y-patterned *27*

(Moray)
Yellow-margin *25*
Yellow-mouth *25*
Zebra *27*
MORAY EELS *24*
MUGILIDAE *154*
Mullet *154*
MULLETS *154*
MULLIDAE *115*
Mulloidichthys *117*
flavolineatus *117*
vanicolensis *117*
MURAENIDAE *24*
Myrichthys *30*
colubrinus *30*
maculosus *30*
MYRIPRISTINAE *41*
Myripristis *45*
adusta *47*
berndti *46*
botche *47*
kuntee *46*
murdjan *46*
pralinia *45*
violacea *46*
vittata *45*
NASINAE *218*
Naso *225*
brachycentron *227*
brevirostris *226*
hexacanthus *228*
lituratus *225*
thynnoides *228*
tuberosus *227*
unicornis *226*
vlamingii *226*
Naucrates *95*
ductor *95*
Needlefish *34*
Crocodile *34*
Schooling *34*
Slender *34*
NEEDLEFISHES *34*
Nemanthias *73*
carberryi *73*
Nemateleotris *215*
decora *215*
magnifica *215*
NEMIPTERIDAE *99*
Neoniphon *43*
argenteus *44*
aurolineatus *44*
opercularis *44*
sammara *43*
Neopomacentrus *147*
cyanomos *147*
Novaculichthys *158*
taeniourus *158*
Odonus *238*
niger *238*
Oedalechilus *154*
labiosus *154*
OPHICHTHIDAE *29*
Ophichthys *29*
bonaparta *29*
OPHIDIIDAE *35*
Oplopomops *206*
atherinoides *206*
Oplopomus *205*
caninoides *205*
oplopomus *205*
OSTRACIIDAE *242*

Ostracion *242*
cubicus *242*
meleagris *242*
Oxycheilinus *176*
arenatus *176*
bimaculatus *177*
digrammus *176*
notophthalmus *176*
Oxycirrhites *137*
typus *137*
Oxymonacanthus *232*
longirostris *232*
Paracaesio *111*
sordidus *111*
Paracanthurus *219*
hepatus *219*
Paracheilinus *172*
mccoskeri *172*
Paracirrhites *138*
arcatus *138*
forsteri *139*
Paraluteres *233*
prionurus *233*
Parapercis *188*
hexophthalma *188*
millipunctata *188*
schauinslandi *189*
signata *188*
Parapriacanthus *119*
ransonneti *119*
Pardachirus *232*
sp *232*
Parrotfish *180*
Bartail *186*
Black-tip *186*
Blue-barred *187*
Bridled *183*
Dusky *185*
Eclipse *186*
Ember *182*
Five-saddle *183*
Green-blotched *185*
Green-face *184*
Green-snout *185*
Happy *187*
Humphead *181*
Longnose *181*
Rosy-cheek *184*
Seagrass *187*
Shabby *183*
Sheephead *182*
Spinytooth *187*
Starry-eye *187*
Three-colour *184*
Two-colour *180*
PARROTFISHES *180*
Parupeneus *115*
barberinus *116*
bifasciatus *117*
cyclostomus *115*
indicus *117*
macronema *116*
pleurostigma *116*
PEGASIDAE *48*
PEMPHERIDIDAE *119*
Pempheris *119*
schwenkii *119*
vanicolensis *119*
Pervagor *233*
aspricaudus *233*
janthinosoma *233*
Petroscirtes *193*

(Petroscirtes)
mitratus *193*
xestus *193*
Photoblepharon *40*
steinitzi *40*
Pilot Fish *95*
PINGUIPEDIDAE *188*
Pipefish *49*
Blue-stripe *53*
Cheeked *51*
Double-chin *53*
Ghost *49*
Long-snout Stick *52*
Many-bands *52*
Reef-top *51*
Schultz's *51*
Short-bodied *52*
Stick *52*
Yellow-banded *51*
PIPEFISHES *50*
Pisonophis *29*
cancrivorus *29*
Plagiotremus *191*
phenax *191*
rhinorhynchos *192*
tapeinosoma *191*
Platax *135*
boersi *136*
orbicularis *135*
teira *136*
Platybelone *34*
argalus *34*
PLATYCEPHALIDAE *60*
Plectorhinchus *104*
chaetodonoides *105*
gibbosus *105*
obscurus *104*
orientalis *105*
Plectroglyphidodon *151*
dickii *151*
imparipennis *152*
johnstonianus *151*
lacrymatus *151*
leucozonus *152*
Plectropomus *63*
areolatus *63*
laevis *64*
pessuliferus *63*
PLESIOPIDAE *77*
PLEURONECTIDAE *231*
Pleurosicya *211*
elongata *211*
micheli *212*
mossambica *212*
PLOTOSIDAE *35*
Plotosus *35*
lineatus *35*
Pogonoperca *61*
ocellata *61*
POMACANTHIDAE *130*
Pomacanthus *132*
annularis *133*
imperator *132*
semicirculatus *132*
xanthometopon *132*
POMACENTRIDAE *140*
POMACENTRIDAE-1 *140*
POMACENTRIDAE-2 *141*
POMACENTRIDAE-3 *142*
POMACENTRIDAE-4 *145*
POMACENTRIDAE-5 *149*
POMACENTRIDAE-6 *151*

Pomacentrus *145*
caeruleus *145*
chrysurus *146*
indicus *146*
nagasakiensis *146*
pavo *145*
philippinus *146*
Pompano *96*
Black-spotted *96*
Snub-nose *96*
Porcupinefish *248*
Black-spotted *248*
Blotched *248*
Few-spined *249*
Rounded *249*
PORCUPINEFISHES *248*
Possum Wrasse *173*
White-banded *173*
Yellow-banded *173*
PRIACANTHIDAE *79*
Priacanthus *79*
blochii *79*
hamrur *79*
Priolepis *207*
cincta *207*
inhaca *207*
nocturna *207*
PRIONURINAE *218*
Pseudaluteres *233*
nasicornis *233*
Pseudamia *88*
gelatinosa *89*
hayashii *88*
Pseudanthias *73*
bicolor *73*
bimaculatus *74*
cooperi *74*
evansi *75*
hypselosoma *75*
ignitis *75*
n. sp. *74*
parvirostris *76*
pulcherrimus *76*
squamipinnis *76*
Pseudobalistes *237*
flavimarginatus *237*
fuscus *238*
Pseudocheilinus *172*
evanidus *172*
hexataenia *172*
octotaenia *172*
PSEUDOCHROMIDAE *77*
Pseudocoris *159*
yamashiroi *159*
Pseudodax *166*
moluccanus *166*
Pseudojuloides *159*
kaleidos *159*
Pseudoplesiops *77*
sp 1 *77*
Ptereleotris *216*
evides *216*
grammica *217*
hanae(?) *216*
heteroptera *216*
microlepis *216*
sp 1 *216*
zebra *216*
Pterocaesio *113*
chrysozona *113*
lativittata *114*
pisang *114*

(Pterocaesio)
  sp 1 *113*
  tile *114*
  trilineata *114*
Pterois *55*
  antennata *55*
  radiata *55*
  volitans *55*
Pufferfish *243*
  Ambon *244*
  Bennett's *245*
  Black-spotted *246*
  Crowned *243*
  False-eye *244*
  Guineafowl *246*
  Saddled *243*
  Scribbled *245*
  Starry *247*
  Stars-and-Stripes *247*
  Tyler's *244*
  White-spotted *245*
  Yellow-eye *247*
PUFFERFISHES *243*
Puller *142*
  Black-edged *145*
  Black-fin *145*
  Blue-green *142*
  Buff *143*
  Deep-reef *144*
  Double-bar *144*
  Green *142*
  Pemba *143*
  Scaly *144*
  Swallow-tail *143*
  Twin-spot *144*
  Two-tone *143*
  Weber's *144*
  White-finned *143*
PULLERS *142*
Pursemouth *97*
  Black-tip *98*
  Oblong *97*
  Short *98*
  Small-scale *98*
PURSEMOUTHS *97*
Pygmy-goby *207*
  Belly-line *210*
  Cave *209*
  Filamentous *209*
  Green *210*
  Orange-spotted *208*
  Red *208*
  Red-blotched *210*
  Red-lined *208*
  Red-spotted *208*
  Sebree's *210*
  Sharp-eye *209*
  Sparsely-spotted *208*
  Taylor's *209*
  Twin-blotch *209*
  White-line *209*
  White-spotted *210*
  Yellow-spotted *208*
  Yellow-tail *207*
Pygoplites *130*
  diacanthus *130*
Queenfish *95*
  Double-spotted *95*
Rabbitfish *229*
  Chin-strap *229*
  Coral *229*
  Java *230*

(Rabbitfish)
  Schooling *229*
  Sri Lankan *230*
  Starry *229*
RABBITFISHES *228*
Rainbow Runner *95*
Rastrelliger *230*
  kanagurta *230*
Razorfish *159*
  Blue *159*
Red Bass *109*
Reef Basslet *62*
  African *62*
  Pinstriped *62*
Reef-goby *207*
  Banded *207*
  Full-Moon *207*
  Hector's *215*
  Orange-tail *207*
  White-barred *214*
Remora *91*
  remora *91*
REMORAS *91*
Rhabdamia *88*
  cypselura *88*
  gracilis *88*
Rhimomuraena *28*
  quaesita *28*
Rhinecanthus *239*
  aculeatus *239*
  cinereus *239*
  rectangulus *239*
Ribbon Eel *28*
Rock Cod *64*
  Blackfin *66*
  Dusky-banded *65*
  Harlequin *66*
  Leopard *66*
  Orange *65*
  Peacock *65*
  Six-spot *64*
  Tomato *65*
  Vermilion *64*
ROCK CODS *61*
Rockling *35*
  Bearded *35*
Rockskipper *196*
  Rippled *196*
  Thin-lined *197*
Rudderfish *120*
  Brassy *120*
  Snubnose *120*
RUDDERFISHES *120*
SABRETOOTH BLENNIES *191*
Sabretooth Blenny *193*
  Bearded *193*
  Crested *193*
Salarias *196*
  fasciatus *196*
Samariscus *231*
  triocellatus *231*
Sand Diver *189*
  Long-rayed *189*
SAND DIVERS *189*
Sand-Eel *29*
  Black-pitted *29*
Sand-Goby *202*
  African *205*
  Decorated *203*
  Double-spot *204*
  Eye-bar *203*
  Fine-spotted *205*

(Sand-goby)
  Inner-spotted *204*
  Orange-spotted *204*
  Silty *202*
  Sparsely-spotted *206*
  White *206*
Sargocentron *41*
  caudimaculatum *43*
  diadema *42*
  melanospilos *41*
  microstoma *41*
  punctatissimus *42*
  spiniferum *43*
  tiere *42*
  tiereoides *42*
  violaceum *43*
Saurida *38*
  gracilis *38*
  nebulosa *38*
Saury *38*
  Blotched *38*
  Reef *38*
Scad *95*
  Big-eye *95*
  Mackerel *96*
SCARIDAE *180*
Scarus *182*
  capistratoides *186*
  caudofasciatus *186*
  dimidiatus *183*
  festivus *187*
  frenatus *183*
  ghobban *187*
  microrhinos *182*
  niger *185*
  prasiognathus *184*
  psittacus *184*
  quoyi *185*
  rubroviolaceus *182*
  russelli *186*
  scaber *183*
  sordidus *183*
  strongylocephalus *182*
  tricolor *184*
  viridifucatus *185*
Scolopsis *99*
  aurata *99*
  bilineata *99*
  xenochroa *99*
Scomberoides *95*
  lysan *95*
SCOMBRIDAE *230*
SCORPAENIDAE *54*
SCORPAENIDAE-1 *55*
SCORPAENIDAE-2 *57*
Scorpaenodes *57*
  guamensis *57*
  parvipinnis *57*
  varipinnis *57*
Scorpaenopsis *57*
  diabola *57*
  oxycephala *58*
Scorpionfish *57*
  Barchin *58*
  Blotchfin *57*
  Common *57*
  Coral *58*
  Paper *59*
  Shortfin *57*
  Smallscale *58*
SCORPIONFISHES *54, 57*
Seahorse *53*

(Seahorse)
  Common *53*
  Spiny *53*
SEAMOTHS *48*
Sebastapistes *58*
  cyanostigma *58*
  strongia *58*
Selar *95*
  crumenophthalmus *95*
Sergeant *149*
  Black-spot *150*
  Green *150*
  Nine-band *149*
Scissortail *150*
  White-breasted *150*
  Yellow-tail *149*
Sergeant Major *149*
SERGEANTS *149*
SERRANIDAE *61*
SERRANIDAE-1 *61*
SERRANIDAE-2 *63*
SERRANIDAE-3 *73*
Shrimp-Goby *198*
  Black *200*
  Blue-barred *199*
  Broad-banded *201*
  Burgundy *201*
  Crocus *202*
  Diagonal *201*
  Dracula *199*
  Fan *200*
  Pale *202*
  Pink-bar *200*
  Side-spot *200*
  Steinitz's *201*
  Tall-fin *198*
  Twin-spotted *199*
SHRIMPGOBIES *198*
Siderea *28*
  picta *28*
  thyrsoidea *28*
SIGANIDAE *228*
Siganus *229*
  argenteus(?) *229*
  corallinus *229*
  javus *230*
  margaritiferus *228*
  puelloides *229*
  sp *230*
  stellatus *229*
  tetrazona *229*
SILVER BATFISHES *97*
Sleeper-goby *212*
  Black-chin *213*
  Black-lined *213*
  Broad-barred *214*
  False *214*
  Golden-head *214*
  Little *213*
  Six-spot *212*
Snake-Eel *30*
  Banded *30*
  Marbled *30*
  Spotted *30*
Snapper *106*
  Bengal *106*
  Black *110*
  Black-spot *107*
  Black-tail *108*
  Blue-striped *106*
  Fusilier *111*
  Humpback *108*

(Snapper)
Indian 107
Mangrove Jack 108
Midnight 110
Moluccen 107
One-spot 107
Red Bass 109
Red Emperor 109
Two-spot 109
SNAPPERS 106
Soapfish 61
Arrow-headed 62
Lined 61
Snowflake 61
Yellow 62
SOAPFISHES 61
Soldierfish 45
Big-eyed 45
Crimson 46
Epaulette 46
Immaculate 45
Shadowfin 47
Splendid 47
Violet 46
Yellow-fin 46
SOLDIERFISHES 41, 45
Sole 232
Pebble 232
SOLEIDAE 232
SOLENOSTOMIDAE 49
Solenostomus 49
cyanopterus 50
paradoxus 49
sp 1 50
Sphyraena 153
barracuda 153
SPHYRAENIDAE 153
Spinecheek 99
Blue-stripe 99
Golden 99
SPINECHEEKS 99
Sponge-goby 211
Slender 211
Squirrelfish 41
Blue-lined 42
Crown 42
Fine-lined 41
Mouthfin 44
Pink 42
Red-face 43
Sabre 43
Silver 44
Speckled 42
Spotfin 43
Three-spot 41
White-tail 43
Yellow-striped 44
SQUIRRELFISHES 41
Stegastes 152
albifasciatus 152
cf fasciolatus sp 1 152
lividus 153
nigricans 153
Stethojulis 164
albovittata 164
strigiventer 164
trilineata 164
Stonefish 57
False 57
Reef 58
Stonogobiops 199
dracula 199

Strongylura 34
crocodilus 34
leiura 34
Suckerfish 91
Short 91
Slender 91
Sufflamen 239
bursa 240
chrysopterus 240
freanatus 239
Surgeonfish 219
Convict 222
Dusky 223
Eye-line 221
Eye-spot 220
Lieutenant 221
Lined 222
Mimic 223
Night 219
Pale 220
Pencilled 220
Powder-blue 219
Ring-tail 221
Sailfin 224
Spot-face 222
White-spine 221
White-spotted 222
Yellow-fin 220
SURGEONFISHES 218
Sweeper 119
Yellow 119
SWEETLIPS 104
Brown 105
Giant 104
Grey 104
Harlequin 105
Oriental 105
Synanceia 58
verrucosa 58
Synchiropus 197
sp 197
stellatus 197
SYNGNATHIDAE 50
SYNODONTIDAE 38
Synodus 38
binotatus 39
dermatogenys 39
indicus 38
jaculum 39
rubromarginatus 40
variegatus 39
Taenianotus 59
triacanthus 59
Tail 78
Triple 78
Tang 219
Blue 219
Brown 225
Yellow-tail 225
Terapon 78
jarbua 78
TERAPONTIDAE 78
Terelabrus 179
sp 179
TETRAODONTIDAE 243
TETRAROGIDAE 59
Thalassoma 169
amblycephalum 169
hardwicke 169
janseni 169
lunare 170
purpureum 170

(Thalassoma)
quinquevittatum 170
Thysanophrys 60
chiltonae 60
otaitensis 60
Tilefish 90
Blue 90
Blue-saddle 90
Green 90
TILEFISHES 89
Trachinocephalus 40
myops 40
Trachinotus 96
baillonii 96
blochii 96
Trachyrhamphus 52
bicoarctatus 52
TREVALLIES 92
Trevally 92
Banded 93
Bar-cheek 94
Big-eye 92
Black 93
Blue-fin 93
Blue-spined 93
Giant 92
Golden 94
Island 94
Yellow-spotted 94
TRICHONOTIDAE 189
Trichonotus 189
elegans 189
Triggerfish 235
Black 240
Blue 238
Blue-line 241
Boomerang 240
Bridled 239
Clown 236
Gilded 241
Half-moon 240
Indian 240
Oceanic 241
Picasso 239
Starry 235
Strickland's 239
Striped 236
Titan 237
Wedge-tail 239
Yellow-margin 237
Yellow-spotted 238
TRIGGERFISHES 235
Trimma 207
emeryi 207
flammeum 208
naudei 208
sp 1 208
sp 2 208
sp 3 208
sp 4 209
sp 5 209
striatum 208
taylori 209
tevegae 209
TRIPLE TAILS 78
Triplefin 190
Green-head 190
Maldives 190
TRIPLEFINS 190
TRIPTERYGIIDAE 190
TRUMPETERS 78
Trumpetfish 48

TRUMPETFISHES 48
Tuna 230
Dogtooth 230
TUNAS 230
Tylosurus 34
crocodilus 34
Unicornfish 225
Big-nose 226
Blue-spine 226
Hump-nose 227
Humpback 227
One-spine 228
Orange-spine 225
Sleek 228
Spotted 226
Upeneus 118
sp 1 118
taeniopterus 118
tragula 118
Valenciennea 212
cf puellaris 213
helsdingeni 213
parva 213
puellaris 213
sexguttata 212
strigata 214
wardii 214
Vanderhorstia 198
ambanoro 199
ornatissima 199
prealta 198
Variola 67
albimarginata 68
louti 67
WASPFISHES 59
Wetmorella 173
albofasciata 173
nigropinnata 173
Whip-goby 211
Loki 211
White-line 211
WORM GOBIES 215
Worm-goby 217
Black-spot 217
Neon 217
Orange-line 217
Wrasse 155
Adorned 161
African 156
Banded Thicklip 177
Bird 168
Blue Razorfish 159
Blue-lined 164
Blue-nose 159
Blue-ribbon 164
Blue-spot 163
Blue-streak Cleaner 167
Checkerboard 163
Chisel-tooth 166
Cigar 157
Cleaner 167
Clouded 162
Diamond 165
Eight-line 172
Exquisite 171
Half-and-Half 177
Indian White 161
Jansen's 169
Knife 158
Lemon Meringue 161
Leopard 160
Maori 174